Connecting *Quarks*
with the *Cosmos*

Eleven Science Questions for the New Century

Committee on the Physics of the Universe
Board on Physics and Astronomy
Division on Engineering and Physical Sciences
NATIONAL RESEARCH COUNCIL
OF THE NATIONAL ACADEMIES

THE NATIONAL ACADEMIES PRESS
Washington, D.C.
www.nap.edu

THE NATIONAL ACADEMIES PRESS   500 Fifth Street, N.W.   Washington, DC 20001

NOTICE: The project that is the subject of this report was approved by the Governing Board of the National Research Council, whose members are drawn from the councils of the National Academy of Sciences, the National Academy of Engineering, and the Institute of Medicine. The members of the committee responsible for the report were chosen for their special competences and with regard for appropriate balance.

This project was supported by Grant No. DE-FG02-00ER41141 between the National Academy of Sciences and the Department of Energy, Grant No. NAG5-9268 between the National Academy of Sciences and the National Aeronautics and Space Administration, and Grant No. PHY-0079915 between the National Academy of Sciences and the National Science Foundation. Any opinions, findings, and conclusions or recommendations expressed in this publication are those of the author(s) and do not necessarily reflect the views of the organizations or agencies that provided support for the project.

International Standard Book Number 0-309-07406-1
Library of Congress Control Number 2003100888

Additional copies of this report are available from the National Academies Press, 500 Fifth Street, N.W., Lockbox 285, Washington, DC 20055; (800) 624-6242 or (202) 334-3313 (in the Washington metropolitan area); Internet, http://www.nap.edu

and

Board on Physics and Astronomy, National Research Council, NA 922, 500 Fifth Street, N.W., Washington, DC 20001; Internet, http://www.national-academies.org/bpa.

Cover: Artwork ©2002 by Don Dixon/cosmographica.com

Printed in the United States of America

THE NATIONAL ACADEMIES
Advisers to the Nation on Science, Engineering, and Medicine

The **National Academy of Sciences** is a private, nonprofit, self-perpetuating society of distinguished scholars engaged in scientific and engineering research, dedicated to the furtherance of science and technology and to their use for the general welfare. Upon the authority of the charter granted to it by the Congress in 1863, the Academy has a mandate that requires it to advise the federal government on scientific and technical matters. Dr. Bruce M. Alberts is president of the National Academy of Sciences.

The **National Academy of Engineering** was established in 1964, under the charter of the National Academy of Sciences, as a parallel organization of outstanding engineers. It is autonomous in its administration and in the selection of its members, sharing with the National Academy of Sciences the responsibility for advising the federal government. The National Academy of Engineering also sponsors engineering programs aimed at meeting national needs, encourages education and research, and recognizes the superior achievements of engineers. Dr. Wm. A. Wulf is president of the National Academy of Engineering.

The **Institute of Medicine** was established in 1970 by the National Academy of Sciences to secure the services of eminent members of appropriate professions in the examination of policy matters pertaining to the health of the public. The Institute acts under the responsibility given to the National Academy of Sciences by its congressional charter to be an adviser to the federal government and, upon its own initiative, to identify issues of medical care, research, and education. Dr. Harvey V. Fineberg is president of the Institute of Medicine.

The **National Research Council** was organized by the National Academy of Sciences in 1916 to associate the broad community of science and technology with the Academy's purposes of furthering knowledge and advising the federal government. Functioning in accordance with general policies determined by the Academy, the Council has become the principal operating agency of both the National Academy of Sciences and the National Academy of Engineering in providing services to the government, the public, and the scientific and engineering communities. The Council is administered jointly by both Academies and the Institute of Medicine. Dr. Bruce M. Alberts and Dr. Wm. A. Wulf are chair and vice chair, respectively, of the National Research Council.

www.national-academies.org

Preface

The fall 1999 meeting of the National Research Council's (NRC's) Board on Physics and Astronomy (BPA) featured a stimulating science session on the frontiers of research at the intersection of physics and astronomy. National Aeronautics and Space Administration (NASA) administrator Daniel Goldin attended the session and at its conclusion asked the BPA to assess the science opportunities in this interdisciplinary area and devise a plan for realizing those opportunities. Robert Eisenstein, assistant director of the National Science Foundation's (NSF's) Mathematical and Physical Sciences Directorate, and S. Peter Rosen, associate director for high-energy and nuclear physics at the Department of Energy (DOE), expressed their desire to work with NASA and supported the initiation of this study. The Committee on the Physics of the Universe was formed and held the first of its eight meetings in March 2000 (see Appendix A).

Mr. Goldin strongly urged the BPA to finish the report in time for the recommendations to play a role in the science planning of the new administration that would be taking office in 2001. To meet that ambitious goal, the BPA decided to divide the study into two phases: a first phase to assess the science opportunities and a second phase to address the implementation of those opportunities. In carrying out the study, the BPA enlisted the help of the Space Studies Board (SSB).

The charge to the committee was as follows:

> The committee will prepare a science assessment and strategy for this area of research at the intersection of astronomy and physics. The study will encompass astrophysical phenomena that give insight into fundamental physics as well as fundamental physics that is relevant to understanding astrophysical phenomena and the structure and evolution of the universe.
>
> The science assessment will be carried out as the first phase of the study over a period of 1 year. The assessment will summarize progress in ad-

dressing the key research issues facing the research community and evaluate opportunities for further progress. Among the science topics to be included in the science assessment are cosmology, the creation of matter and energy at the initiation of the universe, the dark matter known to pervade the cosmos, the dark energy that appears to be causing the expansion of the universe to accelerate, additional dimensions beyond the usual three of space and one of time, strong-field gravitational physics, very-high-energy cosmic rays, neutrino astrophysics, and extreme physics at black holes and magnetized neutron stars.

The second phase of the study, which will require an additional year of work, will result in a strategy for this interdisciplinary area of research. The strategy will include scientific objectives identified in the first phase along with priorities and a plan of action to implement the priorities, including ways to facilitate continued coordinated planning involving NASA, NSF, DOE, and the research community.

During the first phase, the committee held one open meeting to gather input and to hear from the three sponsoring agencies about their current plans and hopes for this study. It also met twice in closed session to prepare an interim report for phase I (see Appendix A for meeting agendas). Community input was gathered during briefings at meetings of the American Astronomical Society, the American Physical Society (APS), the APS Division of Particles and Fields (DPF), the APS Division of Astrophysics and Nuclear Physics, and the APS Topical Group on Gravitation. The committee chose these divisions because the intersection between astronomy and physics largely touches on nuclear, particle, and gravitational physics. An e-mail announcement inviting public comment was widely distributed through the professional societies and their subunits. The interim phase I report contained the science assessment, which was presented in the form of 11 questions that are ripe for progress. The phase I report was released to the public on January 9, 2001, at the meeting of the American Astronomical Society.

The committee began its second phase, the formulation of a strategy for addressing the 11 science questions, by soliciting ideas from the community. A call for proposals was widely circulated in the community (see Appendix B). Some 80 proposals for projects that address the scientific questions identified in the phase I report were received (see Appendix C). A series of three open meetings was held to hear about projects and ideas. The first was held in association with the April 2001 meeting of the APS; the second was held in conjunction with the June meeting of the American Astronomical Society; and the final meeting was held in Snowmass, Colorado, during the DPF's Future of High-Energy Physics Study. Two closed meetings were held, one in Chicago, Illinois, and one in Irvine, California, to formulate recommendations.

During the 2-year study the committee kept the BPA, SSB, and Committee on Astronomy and Astrophysics (CAA, a standing committee of the NRC) informed by means of periodic progress reports from its chair.

This final report consists of the phase I report, a series of committee recommendations for realizing the science opportunities, and a new chapter (Chapter 7) devoted to how the science objectives can be addressed. It complements the NRC surveys *Physics in a New Era: An Overview* and *Astronomy and Astrophysics in the New Millennium* (both from the National Academy Press, Washington, D.C., 2001). It builds on the science priorities identified in those studies and focuses on areas at the intersection of astronomy and physics that although peripheral to each discipline separately, become important when considered in the context of both. This report, together with the physics and astronomy surveys, provides a clear and comprehensive picture of the exciting and timely science opportunities that exist in physics and astronomy as we enter a new century.

The committee acknowledges BPA program staff members Don Shapero, Timothy Meyer, Michael Moloney, and Joel Parriott, whose extraordinary effort during the rigorous NRC review process enabled the committee to meet a very aggressive prepublication schedule. The committee and I also thank the NRC review coordinator for the phase I report, Martha Haynes, for her willingness to oversee the review process during the busy winter holiday season and the NRC review coordinator for the final report, Kenneth Kellerman, who worked hard to help the committee meet its ambitious schedule.

I end with a personal note. The committee brought together an extraordinary group of astronomers and physicists. The great diversity in scientific backgrounds was more than balanced by an even greater interest in and appreciation of science far from the members' own research interests. The science opportunities before us made every meeting exciting. Working with this group was a pleasure that I will long remember, and I thank the committee for its hard work and commitment to the study.

Michael S. Turner, *Chair*
Committee on the Physics of the Universe

Acknowledgment of Reviewers

This report has been reviewed in draft form by individuals chosen for their diverse perspectives and technical expertise, in accordance with procedures approved by the National Research Council's Report Review Committee. The purpose of this independent review is to provide candid and critical comments that will assist the institution in making its published report as sound as possible and to ensure that the report meets institutional standards for objectivity, evidence, and responsiveness to the study charge. The review comments and draft manuscript remain confidential to protect the integrity of the deliberative process. We wish to thank the following individuals for their review of this report:

David Arnett, University of Arizona,[1,2]
Jonathan Bagger, Johns Hopkins University, [2]
Barry Barish, California Institute of Technology,[2]
Gordon Baym, University of Illinois at Urbana-Champaign,[1,2]
Beverly Berger, Oakland University,[1]
John Carlstrom, University of Chicago,[2]
Marc Davis, University of California at Berkeley,[1]
Sidney Drell, Stanford Linear Accelerator Center,[1]
Richard Fahey, Goddard Space Flight Center,[1]
Wendy Freedman, Carnegie Observatories,[1,2]
David Gross, University of California at Santa Barbara,[1]
Alice Harding, Goddard Space Flight Center,[1]
Steve Kahn, Columbia University,[2]
Marc Kamionkowski, California Institute of Technology,[1,2]
Richard Kron, Yerkes Observatory, University of Chicago,[2]
Louis Lanzerotti, Lucent Technologies,[1]
Rene Ong, University of California at Los Angeles,[2]
Anneila Sargent, California Institute of Technology,[1]

Peter Stetson, Dominion Astrophysical Observatory,[1]
Joseph H. Taylor, Jr., Princeton University,[1,2] and
Edward L. Wright, University of California at Los Angeles.[1]

Although the reviewers listed above have provided many constructive comments and suggestions, they were not asked to endorse the conclusions or recommendations, nor did they see the final draft of the report before its release. The review of this report was overseen by Martha Haynes,[1] Cornell University, and Kenneth Kellermann,[2] National Radio Astronomy Observatory. Appointed by the National Research Council, they were responsible for making certain that an independent examination of this report was carried out in accordance with institutional procedures and that all review comments were carefully considered. Responsibility for the final content of this report rests entirely with the authoring committee and the institution.

[1,2] Participated in the review for phase 1 or phase 2 of the study or both.

Dedication

The Committee on the Physics of the Universe dedicates this report to a dear friend and valued colleague, David N. Schramm. His vision, research, enthusiasm, and energy helped to open this blossoming area of research, and his strong voice helped bring it to the attention of astronomers and physicists alike. Reproduced below is a viewgraph in his own hand that concisely summarized his vision.

The study of
The very large (Cosmology)
and
The very small (Elementary Particles)

is

coming together

Contents

Executive Summary

We are at a special moment in our journey to understand the universe and the physical laws that govern it. More than ever before astronomical discoveries are driving the frontiers of elementary particle physics, and more than ever before our knowledge of the elementary particles is driving progress in understanding the universe and its contents. The Committee on the Physics of the Universe was convened in recognition of the deep connections that exist between quarks and the cosmos.

THE QUESTIONS

Both disciplines—physics and astronomy—have seen stunning progress within their own realms of study in the past two decades. The advances made by physicists in understanding the deepest inner workings of matter, space, and time and by astronomers in understanding the universe as a whole as well as the objects within it have brought these scientists together in new ways. The questions now being asked about the universe at its two extremes—the very large and the very small—are inextricably intertwined, both in the asking and in the answering, and astronomers and physicists have been brought together to address questions that capture everyone's imagination.

The answers to these questions strain the limits of human ingenuity, but the questions themselves are crystalline in their clarity and simplicity. In framing this report, the committee has seized on 11 particularly direct questions that encapsulate most of the physics and astrophysics discussed here. They do not cover all of these fields but focus instead on the interface between them. They are also questions that we have a good chance of answering in the next decade, or should be thinking about answering in following decades. Among them are the most profound questions that human beings have ever posed about the cosmos. The fact that they are ripe now, or soon will be, further highlights how exciting the possibilities of this moment are. The 11 questions are these:

What Is Dark Matter?

Astronomers have shown that the objects in the universe, from galaxies a million times smaller than ours to the largest clusters of galaxies, are held together by a form of matter different from what we are made of and that gives off no light. This matter probably consists of one or more as-yet-undiscovered elementary particles, and aggregations of it produce the gravitational pull leading to the formation of galaxies and large-scale structures in the universe. At the same time these particles may be streaming through our Earth-bound laboratories.

What Is the Nature of Dark Energy?

Recent measurements indicate that the expansion of the universe is speeding up rather than slowing down. This discovery contradicts the fundamental idea that gravity is always attractive. It calls for the presence of a form of energy, dubbed "dark energy," whose gravity is repulsive and whose nature determines the destiny of our universe.

How Did the Universe Begin?

There is evidence that during its earliest moments the universe underwent a tremendous burst of expansion, known as inflation, so that the largest objects in the universe had their origins in subatomic quantum fuzz. The underlying physical cause of this inflation is a mystery.

Did Einstein Have the Last Word on Gravity?

Black holes are ubiquitous in the universe, and their intense gravity can be explored. The effects of strong gravity in the early universe have observable consequences. Einstein's theory should work as well in these situations as it does in the solar system. A complete theory of gravity should incorporate quantum effects—Einstein's theory of gravity does not—or explain why they are not relevant.

What Are the Masses of the Neutrinos, and How Have They Shaped the Evolution of the Universe?

Cosmology tells us that neutrinos must be abundantly present in the universe today. Physicists have found evidence that they have a small mass, which implies that cosmic neutrinos account for as much mass as do stars. The pattern of neutrino masses can reveal much about how nature's forces are unified, how the elements in the periodic table were made, and possibly even the origin of ordinary matter.

How Do Cosmic Accelerators Work and What Are They Accelerating?

Physicists have detected an amazing variety of energetic phenomena in the universe, including beams of particles of unexpectedly high energy but of unknown origin. In laboratory accelerators, we can produce beams of energetic particles, but the energy of these cosmic beams far exceeds any energies produced on Earth.

Are Protons Unstable?

The matter of which we are made is the tiny residue of the annihilation of matter and antimatter that emerged from the earliest universe in not-quite-equal amounts. The existence of this tiny imbalance may be tied to a hypothesized instability of protons, the simplest form of matter, and to a slight preference for the formation of matter over antimatter built into the laws of physics.

What Are the New States of Matter at Exceedingly High Density and Temperature?

The theory of how protons and neutrons form the atomic nuclei of the chemical elements is well developed. At higher densities, neutrons and protons may dissolve into an undifferentiated soup of quarks and gluons, which can be probed in heavy-ion accelerators. Densities beyond nuclear densities occur and can be probed in neutron stars, and still higher densities and temperatures existed in the early universe.

Are There Additional Space-Time Dimensions?

In trying to extend Einstein's theory and to understand the quantum nature of gravity, particle physicists have posited the existence of space-time dimensions beyond those that we know. Their existence could have implications for the birth and evolution of the universe, could affect the interactions of the fundamental particles, and could alter the force of gravity at short distances.

How Were the Elements from Iron to Uranium Made?

Scientists' understanding of the production of elements up to iron in stars and supernovae is fairly complete. Important details concerning the production of the elements from iron to uranium remain puzzling.

Is a New Theory of Matter and Light Needed at the Highest Energies?

Matter and radiation in the laboratory appear to be extraordinarily well described by the laws of quantum mechanics, electromagnetism, and their unification as quantum electrodynamics. The universe presents us with places and objects, such as neutron stars and the sources of gamma ray bursts, where the conditions are far more extreme than anything we can reproduce on Earth that can be used to test these basic theories.

———————————————

Each question reveals the interdependence between discovering the physical laws that govern the universe and understanding its birth and evolution and the objects within it. The whole of each question is greater than the sum of the astronomy part and the physics part of which it is made. Viewed from a perspective that includes both astronomy and physics, these questions take on a greater urgency and importance.

Taken as a whole, the questions address an emerging model of the universe that connects physics at the most microscopic scales to the properties of the universe and its contents on the largest physical scales. This bold construction relies on extrapolating physics tested today in the laboratory and within the solar system to the most exotic astronomical objects and to the first moments of the universe. Is this ambitious extrapolation correct? Do we have a coherent model? Is it consistent? By measuring the basic properties of the universe, of black holes, and of elementary particles in very different ways, we can either falsify this ambitious vision of the universe or establish it as a central part of our scientific view.

The science, remarkable in its richness, cuts across the traditional boundaries of astronomy and physics. It brings together the frontier in the quest for an understanding of the very nature of space and time with the frontier in the quest for an understanding of the origin and earliest evolution of the universe and of the most exotic objects within it.

Realizing the extraordinary opportunities at hand will require a new, crosscutting approach that goes beyond viewing this science as astronomy or physics and that brings to bear the techniques of both astronomy and physics, telescopes and accelerators, and ground- and space-based instruments. The goal then is to create a new strategy. The obstacles are sometimes disciplinary and sometimes institutional, because the science lies at the interface of two mature disciplines and crosses the boundaries of three U.S. funding agencies: the Department of Energy (DOE), the National Aeronautics and Space Administration (NASA), and the National Science Foundation (NSF). If a cross-disciplinary, cross-agency approach can be mounted, the committee believes that a great leap can be made in understanding the universe and the laws that govern it.

The second part of the charge to the committee was to recommend a plan of action for NASA, NSF, and DOE. In Chapter 7, it does so. First, the committee reviewed the projects in both astronomy and physics that have been started (or are slated to start) and are especially relevant to realizing the science opportunities that have been identified. Next, it turned its attention to new initiatives that will help to answer the 11 questions. The committee summarizes its strategy in the seven recommendations described below.

Within these recommendations the committee discusses six future projects that are critical to realizing the great opportunities before us. Three of them—the Large Synoptic Survey Telescope, the Laser Interferometer Space Antenna, and the Constellation-X Observatory—were previously identified and recommended for priority by the 2001 National Research Council decadal survey of astronomy, *Astronomy and Astrophysics in the New Millennium,* on the basis of their ability to address important problems in astronomy. The committee adds its support, on the basis of the ability of the projects to also address science at the intersection of astronomy and physics. The other three projects—a wide-field telescope in space; a deep underground laboratory; and a cosmic microwave background polarization experiment—are truly new initiatives that have not been previously recommended by other NRC reports. The committee hopes that these new projects will be carried out or at least started on the same time scale as the projects discussed in the astronomy decadal survey, i.e., over the next 10 years or so.

The initiative outlined by the committee's recommendations can realize many of the special scientific opportunities for advancing our understanding of the universe and the laws that govern it, but not within the budgets of the three agencies as they stand. The answer is not simply to trim the existing programs in physics and astronomy to make room for these new projects, because many of these existing programs—created to address exciting and timely questions squarely within physics or astronomy—are also critical to answering the 11 questions at the interface of the two disciplines. New funds will be needed to realize the grand opportunities before us. These opportunities are so compelling that some projects have already attracted international partners and others are likely to do so.

THE RECOMMENDATIONS

Listed below are the committee's seven recommendations for research and research coordination needed to address the 11 science questions.

- **Measure the polarization of the cosmic microwave background with the goal of detecting the signature of inflation. The committee recommends that NASA, NSF, and DOE undertake research and development to bring the needed experiments to fruition.**

Cosmic inflation holds that all the structures we see in the universe today—galaxies, clusters of galaxies, voids, and the great walls of galaxies—originated from subatomic quantum fluctuations that were stretched to astrophysical size during a tremendous spurt of expansion (inflation). Quantum fluctuations in the fabric of space-time itself lead to a cosmic sea of gravitational waves that can be detected by their polarization signature in the cosmic microwave background radiation.

- **Determine the properties of dark energy. The committee supports the Large Synoptic Survey Telescope project, which has significant promise for shedding light on the dark energy. The committee further recommends that NASA and DOE work together to construct a wide-field telescope in space to determine the expansion history of the universe and fully probe the nature of dark energy.**

The discovery that the expansion of the universe is speeding up and not slowing down through the study of distant supernovae has revealed the presence of a mysterious new energy form that accounts for two-thirds of all the matter and energy in the universe. Because of its diffuse nature, this energy can only be probed through its effect on the expansion of the universe. The NRC's most recent astronomy decadal survey recommended building the Large Synoptic Survey Telescope to study transient phenomena in the universe; the telescope will also have significant ability to probe dark energy. To fully characterize the expansion history and probe the dark energy will require a wide-field telescope in space (such as the Supernova/ Acceleration Probe) to discover and precisely measure the light from very distant supernovae.

- **Determine the neutrino masses, the constituents of the dark matter, and the lifetime of the proton. The committee recommends that DOE and NSF work together to plan for and to fund a new generation of experiments to achieve these goals. It further recommends that an underground laboratory with sufficient infrastructure and depth be built to house and operate the needed experiments.**

Neutrino mass, new stable forms of matter, and the instability of the proton are all predictions of theories that unify the forces of nature. Fully addressing all three questions requires a laboratory that is well shielded from the cosmic-ray particles that constantly bombard the surface of Earth.

- **Use space to probe the basic laws of physics. The committee supports the Constellation-X and Laser Interferometer Space Antenna missions, which hold great promise for studying black holes and for testing Einstein's theory in new regimes. The committee further recommends that the agencies proceed with an advanced technology program to develop instruments capable of detecting gravitational waves from the early universe.**

The universe provides a laboratory for exploring the laws of physics in regimes that are beyond the reach of terrestrial laboratories. The NRC's most recent astronomy decadal survey recommended the Constellation-X Observatory and the Laser Interferometer Space Antenna on the basis of their great potential for astronomical discovery. These missions will be able to uniquely test Einstein's theory in regimes where gravity is very strong: near the event horizons of black holes and near the surfaces of neutron stars. For this reason, the committee adds its support for the recommendations of the astronomy decadal survey.

- **Determine the origin of the highest-energy gamma rays, neutrinos, and cosmic rays. The committee supports the broad approach already in place and recommends that the United States ensure the timely completion and operation of the Southern Auger array.**

The highest-energy particles accessible to us are produced by natural accelerators throughout the universe and arrive on Earth as high-energy gamma rays, neutrinos, and cosmic rays. A full understanding of how these particles are produced and accelerated could shed light on the unification of nature's forces. The Southern Auger array in Argentina is crucial to solving the mystery of the highest-energy cosmic rays.

- **Discern the physical principles that govern extreme astrophysical environments through the laboratory study of high-energy-density physics. The committee recommends that the agencies cooperate in bringing together the different scientific communities that can foster this rapidly developing field.**

Unique laboratory facilities such as high-power lasers, high-energy accelerators, and plasma confinement devices can be used to explore physics in extreme environments as well as to simulate the conditions needed to understand some of the most interesting objects in the universe, including gamma-ray bursts. The field of high-energy-density physics is in its infancy, and to fulfill its potential, it must draw on expertise from astrophysics, laser physics, magnetic confinement and particle beam research, numerical simulation, and atomic physics.

- **Realize the scientific opportunities at the intersection of physics and astronomy. The committee recommends establishment of an interagency initiative on the physics of the universe, with the participation of DOE, NASA, and NSF. This initiative should provide structures for joint planning and mechanisms for joint implementation of cross-agency projects.**

The scientific opportunities the committee identified cut across the disciplines of physics and astronomy as well as the boundaries of DOE, NASA, and NSF. No agency has complete ownership of the science. The unique capabilities of all three, as well as cooperation and coordination between them, will be required to realize these special opportunities.

The Committee on the Physics of the Universe believes that recent discoveries and technological developments make the time ripe to greatly advance our understanding of the origin and fate of the universe and of the laws that govern it. Its 11 questions convey the magnitude of the opportunity before us. The committee believes that implementing these seven recommendations will greatly advance our understanding of the universe and perhaps even our place within it.

1

Introduction:
Where We Are and Where We Can Be

Elementary particle physicists and astronomers work at different extremes, the very small and the very large. They approach the physical world differently. Particle physicists seek simplicity at the microscopic level, looking for mathematically elegant and precise rules that govern the fundamental particles. Astronomers seek to understand the great diversity of macroscopic objects present in the universe—from individual stars and black holes to the great walls of galaxies. There, far removed from the microscopic world, the inherent simplicity of the fundamental laws is rarely manifest.

Physicists have extended the current understanding of matter down to the level of the quarks that compose neutrons and protons and their equally fundamental partners the leptons (the electron, the muon, and the tau particle, along with their three neutrino partners). They have constructed an elegant and precise mathematical description of the forces that shape quarks and leptons into the matter that we see around us. While elementary particle physicists cannot predict all the properties of matter from first principles, their theories describe in some detail how neutrons and protons are constructed from quarks, how nuclei are formed from neutrons and protons, and how atoms are built from electrons and nuclei (see Box 1.1).

Astronomers' accomplishments in the realm of the universe are no less impressive. They have shown that the universe is built of galaxies expanding from a big bang beginning. Giant telescopes can see across the universe back to the time when galaxies were born, a few billion years after the big bang. The discovery and the subsequent study of the cosmic microwave background (CMB) radiation (the echo of the big bang) provide a snapshot of the universe when it was only about a half million years old, long before the first stars and galaxies were born. Hydrogen, lithium, deuterium, and helium were produced in nuclear reactions that took place when the universe was seconds old, and their presence today in the quantities predicted by the big bang

BOX 1.1   OUR COSMIC ROOTS

An amazing chain of events was unleashed by the big bang, culminating some 13 billion years later in molecules, life, planets, and everything we see around us. Running the expansion of our universe in reverse, back to the big bang, we can be confident there was a time when it was so hot that the universe was just a soup of the elementary particles. Researchers are beginning to speculate about even earlier times when particles did not even exist and our universe was a quantum mechanical soup of strange forms of energy in a bizarre world of fluctuating geometry and unknown symmetries and even an unknown number of spatial dimensions.

The journey to the universe we know today is depicted in Figure 1.1.1. It began at the end of inflation, when vacuum energy and quantum fuzziness became a slightly lumpy soup of quarks, leptons, and other elementary particles. Ten microseconds later quarks formed into neutrons and protons. Minutes later the cooling fireball cooked the familiar lighter elements of deuterium, helium, helium-3, and lithium (the rest of the periodic table of chemical elements was to be produced in stars a few billion years later). Atoms, with their electrons bound to nuclei, came into existence only a half million years or so later. The cosmic microwave background is a messenger from that era when atoms were formed. Along the way, dark matter particles and neutrinos escaped annihilation because of the weakness of their interactions, and for that reason they are still here today.

The slight lumpiness of the dark matter—a legacy of the quantum fuzziness that characterized inflation—triggered the beginning of the formation of the structure that we see today. Starting some 30,000 years after the beginning, the action of gravity slowly, but relentlessly, amplified the primeval lumpiness in the dark matter. This amplification culminated in the formation of the first stars when the universe was 30 million years old, the first galaxies when the universe was a few hundred million years old, and the first clusters of galaxies when the universe was a few billion years old. As the dark matter clumped, the ordinary matter followed, clumping because of the larger gravitational pull of the more massive dark matter. Ordinary matter would get the final word, as its atomic interactions would eventually allow it to sink deeper and form objects made primarily of atoms—stars and planets—leaving dark matter to dominate the scene in galaxies and larger objects.

This gulf of time between the decoupling of matter and radiation and the formation of the first stars is aptly referred to as the "dark ages." Mountain-top observatories on Earth and the Hubble Space Telescope reveal evidence of the

model confirms that the universe began from a soup of elementary particles. Einstein's magnificent theory of space and time describes gravity, the force that holds the universe together and controls its fate. Using the laws of gravity, nuclear physics, and electromagnetism, astronomers have developed a basic understanding of essentially all the objects they have found in the universe, and a detailed understanding of many.

dark ages: Probe deeply enough into space and back in time with a big telescope, and the result is fewer and fewer galaxies.

As stars and galaxies evolved, enriching their protoplanetary gas clouds and eventually planets with the chemical products of stellar evolution, new possibilities for complexity arose: the chemical and molecular conditions for life. Our cosmic roots are in the stars and what came long before. It is possible now to trace those roots back to the quark soup, but it should be possible to trace them back even further to the quantum fuzziness that might have been their origin during inflation.

FIGURE 1.1.1   The universe today is the product of a long, long chain of events, as shown in this artist's conception of cosmological evolution beginning with the big bang. Scientists are exploring not only the chronological relationships between these events but also the causal connections. Image courtesy of NASA.

These advances owe much to new technology. Optical astronomy has witnessed a millionfold gain in sensitivity since 1900, and a hundredfold gain since 1970. Gains in the ability to view the subatomic world of elementary particles through new accelerators and detectors have been similarly impressive. The exponential growth in computing speed and in information storage capability has helped to translate these detector advances into science breakthroughs. Technology has extended researchers' vision across the entire electromagnetic spectrum, giving them eyes on the universe from radio waves to gamma rays, and new forms of "vision" using neutrinos and gravitational waves may reveal more cosmic surprises. Entirely new detectors never dreamed of before are making possible the search for new kinds of particles.

In pursuing their own frontiers at opposite extremes, astronomers and physicists have been drawn into closer collaboration than ever before. They have found that the profound questions about the very large and the very small that they seek to answer are inextricably connected. Physicists want to know if there are new particles in addition to the familiar quarks and leptons. Astronomers are excited to know, too, because these new particles may be the substance of the dark matter that holds all structures in the universe together—including our own Milky Way galaxy. The path of discovery for astronomers now includes accelerators and other laboratory experiments, and the path for physicists now includes telescopes both on the ground and in space.

In their quest for further simplicity and unity in the subatomic world, particle theorists have postulated the existence of additional space-time dimensions. These putative new dimensions in space might explain why the expansion of the universe seems to be speeding up rather than slowing down and might provide the underlying mechanism for the tremendous burst of growth known as inflation that astronomers believe occurred during the earliest moments of creation. If they exist, these new dimensions are well hidden, and the hunt for them will involve both astronomers and physicists.

Even in the testing of well-established laws of nature—such as those of electromagnetism, gravity, and nuclear physics—physicists are joining with astronomers to use the universe as a laboratory to probe regimes of high temperature, high density, and strong gravity that cannot be studied on Earth. Both astronomers and physicists have a stake in knowing whether or not nature's black holes are described accurately by Einstein's theory of gravity and to find the answers, they will have to work together.

More than ever before, breakthrough discoveries in astronomy and physics are occurring at the boundary of the two disciplines. For example, in 1998 physicists working with astronomers and using telescopes announced evidence that the expansion of the universe is speeding up, not slowing down, as had been expected. If the expansion is indeed accelerating, it must be because of dark energy, a mysterious form of energy heretofore unknown. Determining the nature of the dark energy is key to understanding the fate of the universe and may well be important to understanding the quantum nature of gravity as well. While the nature of the dark energy is a "physics" question, astronomers are very interested in the answer, and their telescopes will likely play the critical role.

We stand poised to make great progress in our understanding of the universe and the laws that govern it by connecting quarks with the cosmos. To do so we will need an integrated approach, both interdisciplinary and interagency. Parsing the science into the traditional categories of physics and astronomy and working narrowly within agencies and without coordination and cooperation will not realize the full science potential. In fact, it is important to note that in practice the physicist and the astronomer are often the same individual, and that the boundaries between the disciplines are generally indistinct. These boundaries are particularly difficult to apply to the practitioners of the interfacial science that is the subject of this report.

There are encouraging signs that existing disciplinary and organizational obstacles can be overcome. Physicists and astronomers, and NASA and DOE, are working together on the Gamma-ray Large Area Space Telescope (GLAST), an instrument that will search for evidence of dark-matter annihilations and additional space-time dimensions as well as supermassive black holes and pulsars. The Cryogenic Dark Matter Search (CDMS), whose goal is to detect the dark matter particles that hold our own galaxy together, is supported by both the Division of Physics and the Division of Astronomical Sciences at NSF and by the Office of High Energy and Nuclear Physics at DOE.

But there have been missed opportunities. While many of the pioneering ideas and experiments at the interface of physics and astronomy originated in the United States, many of the most important discoveries occurred elsewhere. For instance, in spite of the fact that the prototypes for the large underground detectors located in Europe and in Japan—which have shown that neutrinos may have enough mass to account for some of the dark matter—were developed in the United States, U.S. scientists and institutions did not lead these exciting and important discoveries. Just as it will take the combined efforts of astronomers and physicists to realize these opportunities, so also each of the three agencies has an important and unique role to play in the scientific adventure that links the extremely large and the extremely small.

In this report the Committee on the Physics of the Universe identifies the most important and timely science opportunities at the intersection of physics with astronomy. Because of the interconnectedness of the science, which is an integral part of its richness, organizing the report into linear chapters was a challenge—no approach would allow each chapter to stand as a discrete element independent of the other chapters. The idea that elementary particles may constitute the bulk of the matter in the universe arises in several contexts—in discussions of both the evolution of the universe and the quest to unify the forces and particles, and in a chapter devoted to dark matter and dark energy. The committee hopes that readers of its report will thereby come to appreciate the many threads that connect the science of the quarks and the science of the cosmos.

Chapter 2, "Foundations: Matter, Space, and Time," provides the intellectual foundation for the four chapters that follow and is by far the most challenging chapter for nonexperts. Chapter 3 addresses opportunities for deepening researchers' understanding of the fundamental forces and particles and of how gravity can be taken beyond Einstein. Chapter 4 deals with the earliest beginnings of the universe. Scientists are poised not only to extend current understanding of the universe back to a time when even the largest structures in the universe were subatomic quantum fluctuations, but also to make profound advances in how matter, space, and time are viewed. The bulk of the stuff in the universe—dark matter and dark energy—lies between the stars and galaxies and is mysterious. As Chapter 5 discusses, the solution to the dark matter problem very likely involves one (or more) new particles of nature, and astronomers and physicists are now poised to solve this 70-year-old puzzle. At the same time, a joint effort is needed to tackle the dark energy problem. Chapter 6 deals with the opportunities that lie ahead to use the universe as a laboratory to study the physical laws—of nuclear physics, gravity, and electromagnetism—in regimes beyond the reach of terrestrial laboratories, and even, possibly, to discover new laws. Chapter 7, the final chapter, summarizes the scientific opportunities identified by the committee in the form of 11 questions that are deep in their content, crosscutting, and ripe for answering. The chapter goes on to recommend a strategy for realizing the opportunities. The strategy is summarized in the committee's seven recommendations at the end of the chapter. Appendix D is a glossary that also contains definitions of acronyms.

This is a special moment. If we can take advantage of the opportunities that exist, we stand to make truly fundamental advances in our understanding of how the universe began as well as of the basic nature of matter, space, and time. Because of the deep and profound connections between quarks and the cosmos, advances in both are inextricably connected and taking will require a new approach that lies at the boundary of physics and astronomy.

2

Foundations: Matter, Space, and Time

BACKGROUND

In the first half of the 20th century the twin revolutions of quantum theory and relativity dramatically changed scientists' perspective on the physical world. Building on this base, over the last half of the 20th century physicists developed and tested a new quantum theory of matter (now called the Standard Model) and extended and tested the theory of classical space-time (general relativity and big bang cosmology). These successes present extraordinary new opportunities for physics in the new century. Questions of unprecedented depth and scope about the ultimate laws governing physical reality, and about the origin and content of the physical universe, can now be formulated and addressed—and possibly even answered! Is there a unified theory encompassing all the laws of physics? Is matter fundamentally unstable? Are there additional dimensions of space? Is most of the mass in the universe hidden in some exotic form? Does "empty" space have energy (a cosmological constant term in the equations of general relativity)? What physical principle determines that energy?

Today physicists and astronomers have some specific, compelling ideas about the answers to these grand questions. These ideas are by no means vague and idle speculations. On the contrary, they are grounded, scientific hypotheses, testable by performing appropriate experiments and observations. To test such concepts is a challenging task—all the easy work and much of the very difficult (but possible) work has already been done, and what was learned has been incorporated into current knowledge. To probe situations further where established theories are not adequate requires producing and observing matter under extraordinary new conditions or exploiting novel techniques to see in new ways or to new places. Fortunately, there are some highly creative ideas—and timely opportunities—for accomplishing such exploration. This chapter outlines the intellectual context within which the rest of this report can be understood. Later chapters focus more directly on the opportunities now available to begin to answer the 11 questions on the nature, origin and makeup of our universe.

PHYSICS OF MATTER: THE STANDARD MODEL AND BEYOND

The Standard Model

The Standard Model is a modest name for a grand intellectual achievement. For it is no less than, and in many ways more than, the theory of the fundamental structure of known matter. At the beginning of the 20th century, physics was very different from today. The classical laws of that time allow one to predict, given the configuration of matter and force fields at one time, the configurations at all later times. For example, Newton's laws of motion and gravitational attraction can predict the positions of planets and comets in the future once their current positions (and velocities) are known. However, nothing in Newton's laws can predict the existence of, or determine the overall size or shape of, the solar system. The modern (20th century) laws of physics go well beyond simple extrapolation of known conditions to the future. They describe not only how things move, but also what sorts of things there can and cannot be.

The first theory of the new type was the mathematical atomic model proposed by Niels Bohr in 1913. At first glance this model appears to differ little in spirit from Newton's solar system or Rutherford's nuclear atom: electrons orbit an atomic nucleus just as planets orbit the sun; the relevant force is electric rather than gravitational but obeys a similar law that relates force and distance between objects. But Bohr postulated that only certain orbits of definite size and shape could actually occur—the orbits are *quantized*. With this idea it became possible to explain why all systems with one electron orbiting one proton have exactly the same properties, and to calculate those properties. Thus, the universal properties of the substance called hydrogen could be explained. The existence of such a substance, with all its properties, is a consequence of the allowed quantum solutions for the interactions between a proton and an electron.

Bohr's original rules, though successful in describing many features of atomic spectra, were not entirely correct, nor even internally consistent. Later physicists, including Werner Heisenberg, Erwin Schrodinger, and Paul Dirac, produced a framework that corrected these problems for the dynamics of quantized systems. The new quantum mechanics of simple electrical forces between elementary electrons and nuclei could explain the main features of atoms and thus—in principle—all of chemistry. The mature form of the theory, unifying both electrodynamics and quantum mechanics, is called quantum electrodynamics, or QED for short. According to this theory, the electrical and magnetic forces and energy are carried by photons, which are quantum excitations of the electromagnetic fields (see Box 2.1).

Despite such revolutionary breakthroughs, major challenges remained. There were still subtle internal difficulties within QED. All the many successful applications of QED were based on solving the equations in an approximate way. When physicists tried to solve the equations more precisely, they ran into great difficulties. Some corrections seemed to be infinite! Thus, although QED was spectacularly successful at a practical level, it was completely unsatisfactory from a logical point of view, because it required setting infinite quantities to zero. This mathematically dubious procedure amounted to ignoring a physical effect called quantum fluctuations, the quantum mechanical corrections to the theory. Eventually it was recognized that the problem lay in the interpretation of the quantum corrections, not just in how they affected the particle processes but also in how they altered the concept of empty space or the vacuum. Since these effects have a role to play later in this story, it is worth taking a little time here to discuss them.

One of the revolutionary aspects of quantum mechanics was Heisenberg's uncertainty principle, which specifies a limit to how precisely one can measure both the position of a particle and its momentum (or

BOX 2.1   PARTICLES AND FIELDS

Quantum electrodynamics (QED) was the first example of a field theory of how matter interacts with light. All subsequent particle theories are built to include QED, and are likewise field theories. In field theories each particle type is understood as the quantum excitations of some underlying field type. Conversely, the excitations for every type of field include an associated particle type. Thus the fact that all particles also have associated wavelike properties comes from the fact that both particlelike and wavelike excitations of the underlying fields can occur.

In such theories, the key distinction between matter fields and force fields is the spin (i.e., the amount of angular momentum) associated with the particle excitations of the field. For matter fields the associated particles are fermions, which means that they carry one-half unit of spin (measured in terms of Planck's constant, h), while the photon carries one whole unit of spin. The particles associated with strong and weak force fields, the gluon and W/Z bosons respectively, also carry one unit of spin, while the predicted particle associated with excitation of the Higgs field has zero spin.

velocity) at the same moment. Put another way, an attempt to examine very closely where a particle is located, is accompanied by a large uncertainty in the knowledge of its momentum, in particular whether it may be moving very rapidly. These unpredictable motions represent "quantum fluctuations" in the particle's motion. The special theory of relativity requires a similar uncertainty principle involving time instead of position, and energy instead of momentum. Thus if a particle—or even "empty" space—is observed for a very short time, it is not possible to measure precisely the amount of energy contained in the region observed. The amount of energy may appear to be very high, even when what is being observed is empty space, often called the vacuum (see Box 2.2). Thus, over a short enough time, there could appear to be enough energy present to produce particle-antiparticle pairs of various kinds. These evanescent particles, which apparently pop in and out of existence for a short time, are called virtual particles. Quantum mechanics and relativity together force scientists to see empty space in a new way: as a dynamic medium full of virtual particles.

Immediately following World War II, Willis Lamb and other experimenters exploited advances in microwave technology, driven by wartime work on radar, to measure the properties of atomic hydrogen with unprecedented accuracy. They discovered small deviations from the QED predictions that, at the time, ignored quantum corrections. In the 1950s, inspired by these developments, physicists, including Shinichiro Tomonaga, Julian Schwinger, and Richard Feynman, developed new mathematical methods that gave more accurate predictions. Their methods incorporated the quantum corrections in a profound way from the start. They include the possibility for an isolated particle traveling in empty space to "interact with the vacuum" by temporarily disappearing to produce a virtual particle-antiparticle pair, seemingly coming from the vacuum itself. The original particle then reappears when the particle and antiparticle meet and annihilate each other. The intermediate stages in these calculations seem to involve impossible physical processes, but because they last for such a short time they are allowed by the strange logic of quantum uncertainty in energy. These physicists found a technique by which they could incorporate such quantum effects into the way the constants of the theory were defined and thereby obtain meaningful and finite results for the physically measurable quantities they wished to calculate. Furthermore their results matched the measurements. Indeed, the quantitative agreement between the theoretical predictions of QED calculations and experiment is now the most precise in all of science, reaching levels of parts per billion.

BOX 2.2   THE VACUUM: IS EMPTY SPACE REALLY EMPTY?

While the notion of a vacuum brings to mind the ultimate state of nothingness (indeed, this is what was pictured by 19th-century physics), quantum theory changes all of that. Nature's quantum vacuum is anything but empty; instead, it is seething with virtual particles and condensates. To 20th-century physicists, the vacuum is simply the lowest energy state of the system. It need not be empty or uninteresting, and its energy is not necessarily zero.

Quantum mechanics and the uncertainty principle tell scientists that the vacuum can never be truly empty: the constant production and then annihilation of virtual particle-antiparticle pairs make it a seething sea of particles and antiparticles living on borrowed time and energy (as shown in Figure 2.2.1). Although the Heisenberg uncertainty principle allows the pairs to last for only very short times, they have measurable effects, causing shifts in the spectrum of atomic hydrogen and in the masses of elementary particles that have been measured (e.g., W/Z bosons).

The unanswered question is whether empty space contains any energy. The weight of the vacuum is certainly not great enough to influence ordinary physical processes. However, its cumulative effect can have profound implications for the evolution of the universe and may in fact be responsible for the fact that the expansion of the universe seems to be speeding up rather than slowing down (see the discussion of dark energy in Chapter 5).

The second way in which the vacuum may not be empty involves vacuum condensates of fields. For example, the Higgs field in the Standard Model has a nonzero, constant value in the lowest energy state. The effect of this is to give masses to quarks, leptons, and other particles. The lowest state, the one we perceive as "nothing," need not have zero field. Rather, the field everywhere has the value that gives the minimum energy. The nonzero field in the vacuum is often called a condensate, a term borrowed from condensed-matter physics.

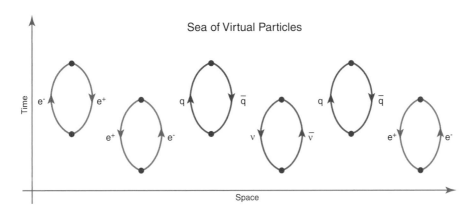

FIGURE 2.2.1   **According to the rules of quantum field theory, the vacuum is not empty but it is actively populated by particle-antiparticle pairs that appear, annihilate, and disappear, existing for only brief instants.**

Successful as it is at describing atomic-level processes, QED is not a complete theory of matter. The basic properties of nuclei are not described by QED. Additional interactions, which cannot be either electromagnetic or gravitational, must also exist. These interactions must be strong enough to hold together the positively charged atomic nucleus. These most powerful of all forces, the strong interactions, are also important in understanding the dynamics of astrophysical objects and of the earliest moments of the universe.

Nuclear decays also exhibit processes wherein one kind of particle turns into another. The prototype for this is the decay of a neutron into a proton, electron, and antineutrino, but there are many closely related processes (including the radioactive decay of the famous isotope carbon-14). Collectively, these weak interactions (so-called because they occur very slowly compared with strong reactions) are central to astrophysics and cosmology. They provide some of the mechanisms for fusion processes by which stars produce energy and build chemical elements heavier than hydrogen.

Thus the weak and the strong interactions are essential to understanding the structure and decay of nuclei and their formation in stellar and early universe environments. However, they are difficult to study in everyday settings because the distances over which they are detectable are incredibly small. In constructing QED, physicists were able to use the rules of electricity and magnetism derived from studying visible objects (pith balls, magnets, coils, and so on) in the late 18th and early 19th centuries. These had been consolidated into the unified equations of electromagnetism by James Clerk Maxwell in 1864. Amazingly, these same equations, interpreted in the framework of quantum mechanics, describe atomic physics. In contrast, to study weak and strong interactions and thereby understand subnuclear processes, physicists had to invent new tools. They ultimately developed tools for studying processes occurring on incredibly tiny distance scales (a thousand times smaller than an atomic nucleus). The story of how such experiments developed, and the remarkably complete understanding achieved, is rich and complex, but this is not the place to relate it fully.

In the early days, naturally occurring radioactive elements and cosmic rays from outer space played a central role. Over the past 50 years, particle accelerators, with a steady increase in the energy of the available particle beams, have been essential. The great scientific achievements of these machines, and the development of the Standard Model theory to incorporate their discoveries, would not have been possible without generous support from government agencies worldwide. Some important aspects of this modern theory of the strong, weak, and electromagnetic interactions are discussed in Box 2.1; Figure 2.1 provides an inventory of the small number of fundamental particles and their simple properties. To the best of current knowledge it appears that these particles have no substructure, at least not in the traditional sense of being built from yet smaller particles. Attempts to simplify the picture by this approach have failed, and no experimental evidence to date points in that direction.

Two essential conceptual features of the Standard Model theory have fundamentally transformed the understanding of nature. Already in QED the idea arose that empty space may not be as simple a concept as it had seemed. The Standard Model weak interaction theory takes this idea a step further. In formulating that theory, it became evident that the equations did

FERMIONS matter constituents spin = 1/2, 3/2, 5/2, ...						**BOSONS** force carriers spin = 0, 1, 2, ...					
Leptons spin = 1/2			**Quarks** spin = 1/2			Unified Electroweak spin = 1			Strong (color) spin = 1		
Flavor	Mass GeV/c²	Electric charge	Flavor	Approx. Mass GeV/c²	Electric charge	Name	Mass GeV/c²	Electric charge	Name	Mass GeV/c²	Electric charge
ν_e electron neutrino	<1×10⁻⁸	0	u up	0.003	2/3	γ photon	0	0	g gluon	0	0
e electron	0.000511	−1	d down	0.006	−1/3	W⁻	80.4	−1			
ν_μ muon neutrino	<0.0002	0	c charm	1.3	2/3	W⁺	80.4	+1			
μ muon	0.106	−1	s strange	0.1	−1/3	Z⁰	91.187	0			
ν_τ tau neutrino	<0.02	0	t top	175	2/3						
τ tau	1.7771	−1	b bottom	4.3	−1/3						

PROPERTIES OF THE INTERACTIONS

Property \ Interaction	Gravitational	Weak (Electroweak)	Electromagnetic	Strong	
				Fundamental	Residual
Acts on:	Mass – Energy	Flavor	Electric Charge	Color Charge	See Residual Strong Interaction Note
Particles experiencing:	All	Quarks, Leptons	Electrically charged	Quarks, Gluons	Hadrons
Particles mediating:	Graviton (not yet observed)	W⁺ W⁻ Z⁰	γ	Gluons	Mesons
Strength relative to electromag for two u quarks at: 10⁻¹⁸ m	10⁻⁴¹	0.8	1	25	Not applicable to quarks
3×10⁻¹⁷ m	10⁻⁴¹	10⁻⁴	1	60	
for two protons in nucleus	10⁻³⁶	10⁻⁷	1	Not applicable to hadrons	20

FIGURE 2.1   Standard Model particles and the forces by which they interact. The fundamental particles include both fermions, the matter particles, and bosons, the force carriers. Masses of all particles are given in GeV/c², a unit in which the mass of the proton is approximately 0.94; electric charge is listed in units of the electron's charge. The Higgs particle has not yet been observed; if it is, it will join the bosons. As is discussed in Chapter 3, it now appears likely that the model needs to be extended to allow small neutrino masses. Image courtesy of the Particle Data Group, Lawrence Berkeley National Laboratory.

not allow the introduction of mass for the particles. The theory made sense—that is, it gave finite predictions for some measurable effects, but only if it was written so that each and every fundamental particle had zero mass. But this was not the case experimentally. However, the zero-mass prediction depended on the assumption that the vacuum state was empty, with all fields having everywhere zero value. Physicists realized the theory could be constructed more like the real world by introducing a pervasive condensate into this simplest of pictures. A condensate in elementary particle physics corresponds to the circumstance where the lowest energy state has a nontrivial property; for instance, instead of having zero field value everywhere, the lowest energy state is filled with a particular nonzero value for the field. (The term is coined from the notion that the field "condenses" in the low-energy limit to a nonzero value.) In the Standard Model the field that forms such a condensate is called the Higgs field. Particles get their mass through interactions with this field. In such a theory, mass is just another form of interaction energy.

But what does it mean to have a nonzero field in the vacuum? In a crude but useful analogy, it is as if we lived inside a giant invisible magnet. Imagine for a moment how the laws of physics would look to people inside such a magnet. Particles would move in peculiar helical paths because of the influence of the magnetic field, and the equations describing these paths would be complicated. Therefore, the laws of motion for a particle subjected to no perceived force would be considerably messier than a straight line. Eventually the inhabitants might realize that they could get a simpler, yet more profound, understanding of nature by starting with the fundamental equations for an empty, nonmagnetic world and then specializing the equations to take account of the complicated medium.

The theory of the weak interaction uses a similar idea. Instead of a pervasive magnetic field, the theory leads to a need for a less familiar background: the Higgs condensate. But unlike magnetic fields, the Higgs field has no preferred direction. It changes the way particles move through space in the same way for all directions of motion. The presence of pervasive condensates is an additional way, beyond the bubbling in and out of existence of virtual particles, that seemingly empty space acts as a dynamical medium in modern quantum theories. Aside from its effect on particle masses, the Higgs condensate is not noticeable in any way because it is everywhere the same. The things observed as particles are differences in the fields from their vacuum values. The theory predicts Higgs particles—fluctuations of the Higgs field away from its constant vacuum value—in just the same way as fluctuations of other fields away from their zero vacuum value are seen as particles. The Higgs particle is the only particle type predicted by the Standard Model that has not yet been observed.

The modern theory of the weak interactions achieved its mature form around 1970 with a unified description of the weak and electromagnetic interactions (sometimes called electroweak theory). Since then, it has achieved many triumphs. Five fundamental particles predicted by the theory, namely the charm and top quarks, the tau neutrino, and the W and Z bosons, have been discovered. The theory predicted many properties of each of these particles; they were found as predicted. For the W and the Z boson, the masses (around 100 times that of the proton) were a key part of the structure of the theory. The existence and properties of W and Z bosons were inferred from a theory designed by Sheldon Glashow, Abdus Salam, and Steven Weinberg. These particles were subsequently discovered experimentally by Carlo Rubbia, Simon van der Meer, and their collaborators, at the European Organization for Nuclear Research (CERN).

The theory of the strong interaction began to take its modern shape once it was realized that all the observed strongly interacting particles (baryons and mesons) could be explained as built from more elementary building blocks: the quarks. Compelling evidence for quarks came from experiments that directly measured the fractional electrical charge and other properties of these pointlike constituents of protons, neutrons, and mesons (these and particles like them are collectively called hadrons). However, the interactions among the quarks had to have very peculiar properties. The strength (or intensity) of these interactions must be tiny when the quarks are close together, but must grow enormously in strength as the quarks are pulled apart. This property, requiring infinite energy to move two quarks completely away from each other, explains why individual quarks are never observed: they are always found bound in triads (as in the proton and neutron and other baryons) or paired with antiquarks (as in the mesons). Although required by the observations, this force between quarks was a new pattern. Physicists had great difficulty finding a consistent theory to describe it. All previous experience, and all simple calculations in quantum field theory, suggested that forces between particles always grow weaker at large separation.

A solution to the problem was found in the quantum correction effects mentioned above, which must be included in a correct calculation. For most theories examined up until that time, this effect also leads to forces that grow weaker at larger distances. However, physicists found a class of theories in which quantum corrections have just the opposite effect: forces grow weaker at small distances. This property is called asymptotic freedom.

With the need for asymptotic freedom in explaining the strong interaction, a unique theory emerged, one that could explain many observations. It introduces particles called gluons as the carriers of the strong force (just as photons carry electromagnetic forces). The "charge" of the strong interactions, called the color charge because of superficial similarities to the familiar properties of visual color, is held by quarks and antiquarks and also by gluons. But all observed hadrons are combinations of these particles in which the total "color" is neutral (much as suitable combinations of primary colors yield white). This theory, which describes the strong interactions, is an essential part of the Standard Model and was dubbed quantum chromodynamics, or QCD.

Since achieving its mature form in the 1970s, QCD has explained many observations and correctly predicted many others (see Figure 2.2 for an

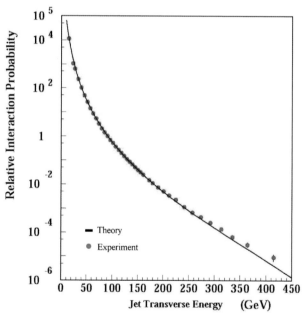

FIGURE 2.2   An example of one of the many successes of the quantum chromodynamics (QCD) sector of the Standard Model. Shown are theoretical predictions (black solid curve), which agree well with experimental data (red points) over 11 orders of magnitude. The data come from high-energy proton-antiproton collisions at Fermilab's Tevatron. The plot shows the relative rate of quark and gluon jet production carrying energy of the amount shown on the horizontal axis, in a direction transverse to the incoming proton and antiproton directions. Adapted from an image courtesy of the D0 Collaboration.

example of QCD's success). Highlights include the discovery of direct effects of gluons, verification of the asymptotic freedom property and its consequences in many and varied experiments, and continued success in modeling the outcomes of high-energy collision processes. Together with the weak interaction theory, QCD is now a firmly established part of the Standard Model.

The story of how experimental evidence for the top quark (also called the *t* quark) was discovered provides an impressive illustration of the power of the Standard Model. The patterns of the electroweak interaction required such a particle to exist and specified how it would decay. Further, as mentioned above, calculation of its indirect effect on well-measured quantities, via quantum corrections, predicted an approximate value for its mass. The strong interaction part of the Standard Model predicted the easiest methods by which it could be produced and how often. Equally important, since QCD describes other particle production processes as well, physicists could calculate the rates for various other processes that can mimic the process of *t* production and decay. This knowledge enabled them to devise a way to search for it in which these competing processes were minimized. This capability is vital, because the relevant events are extremely rare—less than one in a trillion collisions! By putting all this information together, physicists were able to develop appropriate procedures for the search. In 1995, the top quark was discovered in experiments done at Fermilab, as illustrated in Figure 2.3. While its mass was unexpectedly large (about that of an atom of gold), its other properties were as predicted.

The Standard Model has now been tested in so many ways, and so precisely, that its basic validity is hardly in question. It provides a complete description of what kinds of ordinary matter can exist and how they behave under ordinary conditions, with a very broad definition of "ordinary." It certainly extends to any conditions attained naturally on Earth, and even to most astrophysical environments, including the interior of stars. In this sense, it is very likely the definitive theory of known matter, and this marks an epoch in physics. To solve the equations in useful detail in complicated situations is another question. Particle physicists make no claim that achieving this theory of matter answers the important practical questions posed by materials scientists, chemists, or astrophysicists.

Significant challenges remain to complete the Standard Model and understand all that it implies. The Higgs particle is yet to be found. Intense, focused research programs are planned to search for it, both at Fermilab and at the Large Hadron Collider at CERN. The equations of QCD must be solved with greater accuracy in more complicated (and real) situations.

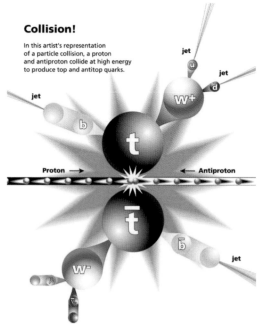

Collision!

In this artist's representation of a particle collision, a proton and antiproton collide at high energy to produce top and antitop quarks.

FIGURE 2.3   The Tevatron at the Fermi National Accelerator Laboratory collides protons and antiprotons with high enough energy to bring the constituent quarks very close together, allowing them to interact. Occasionally, a pair of top quarks is produced, each of which has about the mass of a gold atom. The top quarks quickly decay further into lighter particles. The Collider Detector Facility (above) and the D0 detector (right) are two experiments located at different points where the particles are brought into collision. Images courtesy of Fermilab.

Such calculations have many potential applications. For example, to understand the properties of neutron star interiors and supernova explosions, QCD must be used to calculate the behavior of matter at higher densities than can be achieved in the laboratory. Advances in computer hardware and software, as well as in theoretical understanding, are crucial to maintaining the progress now under way.

A remarkable consequence of the Standard Model, and particularly the asymptotic freedom property, is that the laws can be extended or extrapolated without contradiction well beyond conditions where the model has been tested directly. In fact, the equations become simpler and easier to solve at extremely high energy or temperature. This newfound ability to describe matter in extreme conditions has revolutionized understanding of the very early universe. The big bang picture, the basis of modern cosmology, postulates that extraordinarily high temperatures were attained in the very early universe. The Standard Model permits the calculation with reasonable confidence of how matter behaves in circumstances present at very early times after the big bang. However, researchers cannot test all of these extrapolations directly. In addition, at the very earliest times, quantum gravitational effects become important and must be treated in concert with all the other interactions.

Fortunately, some extrapolations *can* be tested. In collisions of very-high-energy heavy ions (gold, lead, or uranium) conditions similar to those present 10 microseconds after the big bang can be created. These phenomena are beginning to be studied at the Relativistic Heavy Ion Collider at Brookhaven and will be studied further in the ALICE program at CERN.

Looking Beyond the Standard Model

The Standard Model has brought understanding of the fundamental principles governing matter to an extraordinary new level of beauty and precision. It has been tested in many ways. All details of its predictions must continue to be scrutinized with great care and high critical standards. History teaches us that further clues to the ultimate nature of physical reality can lie at the unexplored limits of such a well-tested and accepted theory. Ideas for extending the theory are readily found, although there is, as yet, no evidence to indicate which, if any, of these ideas are correct.

The core of each part of the Standard Model is a description of how different types of force-carrying bosons respond to charges. For QED it is the photon and electrical charge, for QCD it is the color gluons and color charges, and for the weak interactions it is the W and Z bosons and yet other charges. In this sense, the whole Standard Model is a vast generalization of electrodynamics. It is astounding, but true, that the vast diversity of physical behaviors observed for matter in nature is captured within this circle of ideas.

The deep mathematical and conceptual similarities among theories of the strong, electromagnetic, and weak interactions suggest a larger theory unifying them. Indeed, the structure of the theory seems to invite it. In QED, photons respond to electrical charge but never change it. QCD has gluons that respond to the different quark color charges. But gluons also change the color charge of a quark into a different color charge, because gluons them-selves carry both color charge and anticolor charge. Similarly, a W boson changes the weak charge of matter, for example in the transformation of an electron into a neutrino. Each known boson responds to, and carries or changes, only one particular kind of charge. What could be more natural than to make the theory of matter complete and symmetrical by postulating additional bosons that transform one kind of charge (such as color) into another (such as electric charge), because these additional bosons complete the pattern by carrying both charge types? Mathematically, such extensions appear to be an obvious next step. (See Box 2.3 for a discussion of the general notion of symmetries in physical theories.)

This is a beautiful idea. But does nature use it? There are good reasons to suspect the answer is yes. History shows that the most compelling in-sights have simplified complex physical laws into simpler structures, from Maxwell's unification of electricity and magnetism in 1864 to unification of electromagnetism with weak interactions in the Standard Model a century later.

In the Standard Model, bosons fall into 3 independent groupings or sets, while the fermions fall into no fewer than 15 independent sets. The postu-late of complete symmetry among charges simplifies this situation. The bosons are then organized into a single unified set, while the fermions fall into just three sets (each copies of the other, but with different masses). Theories built to have such a unified approach are called grand unified theories. They predict new effects due to the added bosons.

In such theories the proton is unstable. Its observed stability, with a half-life of not less than 10^{32} years, is a severe constraint on this idea. It means that the new force-carrying bosons predicted to simplify the theory must be very massive indeed, so that their effects will occur slowly enough to be consistent with this limit. Even such very heavy particles, however, could be copiously produced in the very earliest times after the big bang. So the postulate of such interactions changes the view of what might occur at

BOX 2.3 SYMMETRIES IN PHYSICAL THEORIES

In nature, symmetries abound and correspond to the appearance of something (e.g., a 5-point star) being unaffected by a rotation or a reflection. In physics, symmetries are transformations that leave the laws of physics for a system invariant. For example, rotational symmetry is manifested as invariance under redefinition of the spatial coordinates by rotating the axes. In field theories there are many possible types of transformation that lead to invariance. In addition to coordinate redefinitions, there are often symmetries of field redefinitions. For example, consider a field that takes complex number values: If the equations depend only on the absolute value, then the physics will be invariant under changes of the phase of the field.

Symmetries are a powerful tool in physics. They greatly simplify the work of defining a theory and its predictions. Any symmetry imposed on the equations limits the variety of solutions that must be investigated. In addition, as shown by Emmy Noether in 1918, any invariance in the equations under a continuous change of variables engenders a related conservation law in the predictions for physical processes. Thus rotational invariance in the equations leads to conservation of angular momentum, while invariance under complex phase definitions leads to predictions such as the conservation of electric charge. Any such conservation law has powerful consequences in predictions for physical processes. Often the conservation law is first found by observation; this then tells physicists what symmetry property the system possesses.

It is useful to categorize the symmetries of different interactions. The strong interactions have symmetries, and thus conservation laws, that are not preserved by the weak interactions. For example, conservation of the number of particles minus antiparticles of each flavor is observed separately in all strong and electromagnetic processes but not in weak processes. (The different kinds of quarks and leptons are referred to as "flavors.")

Because symmetries are such a successful tool, physicists today try to build theories that have, at some very-high-energy scale, more symmetries than are observed in current experiments. This approach has been used for building the Standard Model itself. Speculative extensions of the Standard Model, known as grand unified theories or as supersymmetric extensions, add even more symmetries.

those times. Another feature of these grand unified theories is that they typically incorporate tiny neutrino masses and predict other effects for neutrinos quite different from Standard Model patterns. Both these features, proton decay and neutrino masses, are discussed further in Chapter 3, which explores the implications of physics beyond the Standard Model in cosmological and astrophysical situations.

Another consequence of the hypothetical symmetry of the grand unified theories is at first glance as much at odds with observation as is proton decay. For mathematical consistency, the strengths of the forces and the radiation rates associated with various kinds of charges must be equal. But the strong force is obviously more powerful than the electromagnetic force. Yet, it is just here at the precipice of paradox that the deepest lessons of the Standard Model come to the rescue. The first lesson, from unification of the electromagnetic and weak interactions, teaches that the true symmetry of the basic equations can be obscured by pervasive condensates. The Higgs condensate was necessary to accommodate particle masses. In the unified theory, an additional condensate is required to make the additional bosons very massive. The existence of the condensate hides the symmetry and makes it appear to be broken.

The second lesson is that the observed force strengths reflect both intrinsic strength and the modification of this strength by quantum corrections. Thus the strength of an interaction changes depending on the energy scale at which the interaction is observed. The perfect symmetry among various charges is spoiled by the condensate, which gives different masses to different particle types. The strengths of the three types of interaction, while the same at extremely high energies, are thus modified differently by quantum corrections and hence can be very different for the energies at which they are observed.

These ideas can be made mathematically precise. Calculations determine how the forces change with energy and whether they can adequately account for the various strengths observed at everyday energies, with a single common strength at very high energy. The parameters of the theory that determine the strength of the forces are called couplings. The result of the calculation of how couplings vary with energy is shown in Figure 2.4. It works remarkably well. Note the extremely large energy scale at which the couplings merge. This sets the scale of the masses for the bosons that mediate proton decay. This is a second remarkable success. Not only do the three couplings merge, but they also do so at an energy scale that is large enough to suppress proton decay. A lower scale could have given a prediction inconsistent with observation, thereby ruling out such theories. In truth, the simplest versions of this idea predicted proton lifetimes that were subsequently excluded by sensitive experiments, but many variants survive this test.

The precise effects of quantum corrections depend on the kinds and the masses of all particles that exist. So the predictions of unification and the observed pattern of couplings may perhaps provide a way to learn something about additional massive particles without actually producing them. This leads to an extremely tantalizing discovery. A rough merging of the three

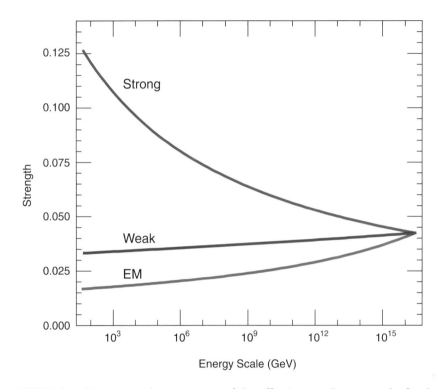

FIGURE 2.4   Variation and convergence of the effective coupling strengths for the three forces—strong, weak, and electromagnetic (EM)—as a function of the energy scale of the interaction. The figure is drawn for a minimal supersymmetric extension of the Standard Model. Without supersymmetry, the three couplings do not precisely meet. Image courtesy of J. Bagger, K. Matchev, and D. Pierce, Johns Hopkins University.

couplings to a single one can be achieved with just the known particles, but the fit is improved by making the theory still more symmetric and encompassing, by incorporating further hypothetical symmetry, known as supersymmetry (see Box 2.4). Figure 2.4 shows the case with these additional particles included. Not only do the couplings all merge cleanly, but also, unlike the version without supersymmetry, the simplest supersymmetric version of the theory predicts a proton half-life that is somewhat above the current lower bound from measurements. Physicists are intrigued by these two results and are actively searching in accelerator experiments for evidence of any of the many additional particles introduced by the postulate of supersymmetry. Of great interest for the physics of the universe is the prediction by supersymmetry of a new, stable weakly interacting particle, known as a neutralino. This

BOX 2.4   SUPERSYMMETRY

Supersymmetry is a bold and profoundly original proposal to extend the space-time symmetry of special relativity. It postulates, in addition to the traditional dimensions of space and time, additional "quantum" dimensions (not to be confused with the extra dimensions of string theory) that together with the traditional dimensions constitute an extended framework for physics called superspace. Each quantum "direction," unlike the continuous space and time directions, has only two discrete values; changing this quantum label is equivalent to changing the particle type! Supersymmetry thus predicts that every particle has a supersymmetric partner particle—normal particles of integer spin have spin one-half partners, while spin one-half particles have integer spin partners, as shown in Figure 2.4.1. Since the matter particles (quarks and leptons) have spin one half and the force carriers (photons, gluons, and W and Z bosons) have spin one, supersymmetry relates the constituents of matter to the particles that mediate the forces that hold matter together.

Not only may supersymmetry unify the matter constituents with the force carriers, but it may also unify gravity with the other forces of nature. Although supersymmetry was invented for other purposes and has a rich history, it is a key element of string theory, the most promising idea that physicists have for incorporating quantum mechanics into gravity and putting gravity on an equal basis with the other forces. Supersymmetry may help to explain the enormous range of energy scales found in particle physics (often referred to as the hierarchy-of-energy-scale problem).

Supersymmetry is mathematically elegant. Nature, however, always has the last word. Is supersymmetry a property of the physical world, or just interesting mathematics? As yet there is no direct evidence for supersymmetry. It is attractive to theorists both for its elegance and because it makes certain features of the Standard Model occur more naturally. At best it is imperfectly realized. Perfect symmetry requires equal mass pairings of particles and their superpartners. No such pairings are found among the known particles, and thus a whole family of superpartners must be postulated. However, valid symmetries of the fundamental laws can be obscured by the existence of pervasive fields (called condensates) in the vacuum. Supersymmetry is such a hidden symmetry. All the superpartners of the known particles can only be as-yet-undiscovered massive particles, and many versions of supersymmetry, in particular those that account best for the merging of the three couplings, predict that these particles should be found at masses accessible with existing or planned accelerators. Searches for these particles may soon reveal or exclude these versions of supersymmetry theory.

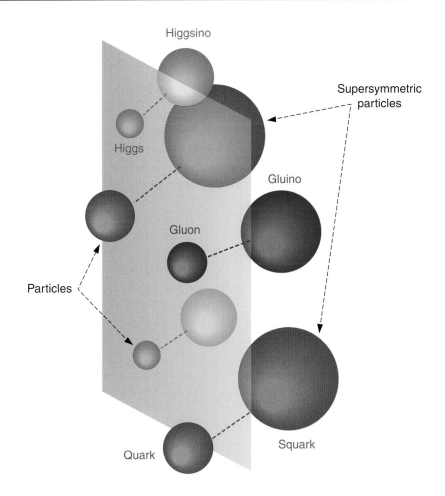

FIGURE 2.4.1 Depiction of the one-to-one correspondence of supersymmetric partner particles for every type of ordinary particle. Because the superpartners are expected to be very massive, they have not yet been directly observed.

particle is a candidate for being the dark matter that pervades the universe. The neutralino is discussed further in later chapters.

PHYSICS OF SPACE AND TIME: RELATIVITY AND BEYOND

The Triumph of General Relativity

When general relativity, Einstein's theory of gravity, was first proposed in 1915, it was a gigantic leap of the imagination. It incorporated several concepts quite new to physics, including the curvature of space-time and the bending of light, and led to the prediction of other completely new phenomena, including gravitational radiation, the expanding universe, and black holes.

General relativity was widely accepted and admired by physicists almost from the start. It reduces to Newton's successful theory of gravity for practical purposes, for not-too-massive bodies moving with small velocities. It is consistent with the special theory of relativity, unlike Newton's theory. Moreover, by relating gravity to space-time curvature, general relativity provided a profound explanation for a striking fact that appears coincidental in Newton's theory: that in a given gravitational field, all bodies accelerate in the same way; this is known as the principle of equivalence or the universality of free fall.

For many years, however, general relativity was not very relevant to the rest of physics; it made few testable new predictions. Only a few observations could not be adequately explained with Newton's simpler theory and thus required the more complete theory. Well into the 1970s, textbooks spoke of only three tests of relativity (namely, the advance of the perihelion of Mercury, the gravitational redshift of light when photons are emitted from the Sun and other massive bodies, and the bending of light by the Sun).

In recent years the picture has changed completely, mainly because of revolutionary improvements in high-precision instrumentation and in the observational techniques of astronomy. The accuracy of each of these three tests now exceeds a part in a thousand, and numerous new precise tests, unimagined by Einstein, have been successfully performed.

Over a thousand neutron stars have been found in the form of pulsars; their gravitational fields can be adequately described using only general relativity. A binary system containing a very remarkable pulsar was discovered in 1976 by Russell Hulse and Joseph Taylor and then studied extensively by Taylor and other collaborators. The orbital motion of the pulsar was measured with great accuracy, thereby enabling precision tests of general relativity. Most dramatic was the observation that as a consequence of the emission of energy into gravitational radiation, the total energy of the orbital motion decreases with time at a rate predicted by general relativity. The agreement is better than one-third of 1 percent. Today, general relativistic corrections to the flow of time on orbiting satellites as compared with the rate on Earth are an essential part of the Global Positioning System (GPS), which allows commercial and military users to calculate a precise location on the surface of the Earth and to transfer accurate time readings using triangulation with satellite signals.

Numerous convincing black hole candidates have been identified through astronomical observations. They fall into two classes. One class, arising from the collapse of stars, has masses ranging from a few times that of the Sun to around 10 times that of the Sun and radii of a few kilometers. The second class, typically found at the centers of galaxies, can have masses millions to billions of times that of the Sun, and radii comparable to that of the solar system. There is compelling evidence that our own galaxy contains such a black hole. It is probable that the most violently energetic objects in the universe, the quasars, are powered by accretion of matter onto such gigantic spinning black holes.

Developments in general relativistic cosmology have been still more remarkable. The theory of the expanding universe has been resoundingly verified by observation of the velocities of distant objects. The gravitational redshift of spectral lines is evolving: once an exotic, difficult test of general relativity, it is becoming a standard tool of astronomy. The bending of light, first observed as a tiny apparent angular displacement for a star with light grazing the Sun during a solar eclipse, is now the basis of a fruitful technique to map dark matter using gravitational lensing. The mass of intervening galaxies is observed, in many cases, to distort the light from more distant sources drastically, even producing multiple images. This provides a way to search for massive objects that produce no light or other detectable radiation. In all these applications, the predictions of general relativity have not been contradicted.

Looking Beyond General Relativity

Despite these great successes, there are compelling reasons to think that general relativity is not the last word on gravity.

A primary stumbling block for understanding the physics of the very earliest moments and the birth of the universe itself is the lack of progress in developing a consistent theory that includes both general relativity and quantum mechanics. The difficulties are similar to, but more severe than, the difficulties discussed above in connection with the history of quantum electrodynamics. All the successful applications of general relativity have used equations that ignore quantum corrections. When the corrections are actually calculated, they are found to be infinite. Again, one can follow the procedure used in QED and improve the calculation by taking into account the effects of virtual particle clouds on, say, the interaction of a particle with gravity. However, although the infinities are then avoided, the ability to calculate the behavior of the particle at high energies is lost, because the clouds interact strongly and in a very complex manner.

Another difficulty arises out of Stephen Hawking's recognition that, when the effects of quantum mechanics are included, black holes are not, strictly speaking, black. Rather they radiate. The radiation rate is far too small to be detectable for any of the known black holes, but it has serious consequences. In Hawking's approximate calculation, the radiation appears to be random (thermal). A fundamental requirement of quantum mechanics is a specific connection between the future and the past. But if black holes, which have swallowed objects carrying quantum information from the past, can evaporate by radiating in a random fashion, this connection is apparently broken. Many believe this leads to a paradox whose ultimate resolution will bring deep insights into the quantum nature of space and time.

While general relativity provides an essential framework for big bang cosmology, it leaves open most of the details, just as Newton's theory described the motion of planets but did not determine the size and shape of the solar system. Indeed, the particular size and shape of our solar system almost certainly arose from the specific details of its history; other planetary systems elsewhere are quite different. Yet the universe as a whole has some strikingly simple features. Such features beg for a theory to explain them.

Among the most striking features of the universe as a whole are its approximate homogeneity and its spatial flatness. Homogeneity means that any large region of the universe of a given age looks very much like any other large region at the same age. Spatial flatness means that space (as opposed to space-time) is not curved on large scales. Both of these properties of the universe have now been observed and measured with considerable precision, through study of the microwave background radiation. Neither homogeneity nor spatial flatness is required by classical general relativity, but they are allowed. The question then arises, Why is our universe so homogeneous and flat? It is possible that these properties would emerge from a correct, quantum-mechanical treatment of the earliest moments of the big bang. But since no one knows how to calculate the behavior of quantum gravity at high energies, such speculation is difficult to test, or even codify.

Some physicists believe that these problems can be solved by delving more deeply into general relativity itself. But others believe that the solution will necessarily involve an integration of gravity with the other forces of nature. As the discussion below indicates, some intriguing progress has recently been made toward a synthesis of general relativity, the theory of space-time, with our current understanding of the other forces of nature.

THE CONVERGENCE OF MATTER AND SPACE-TIME PHYSICS

In most laboratory situations, gravity, as a force between elementary particles, is very much weaker than the strong, the electromagnetic, and even the weak interactions. For this reason, it has been possible to develop an extremely complete and accurate theory of subatomic and subnuclear processes (the Standard Model) while ignoring gravity altogether. But since all objects attract one another gravitationally, the power of gravity is cumulative; on cosmic scales it comes to dominate the other forces. Traditionally, there has been a division of labor between the study of matter, on the one hand, and the study of gravitation and cosmology, on the other. A major theme of this report, however, is that this division is becoming increasingly artificial. Physicists, eager to build on their successful theories of matter and of space-time, seek to create an overarching theory of space-time-matter. To understand the earliest times in the universe and the extreme conditions near black holes will require such a theory. New approaches to tackle these problems are, as yet, speculative and immature. However, the consequences for the view of the universe and for its history at the earliest times are profound.

Inflation

The homogeneity and spatial flatness of the universe can both be explained by assuming that the universe, early in its history, underwent a period of exceptionally rapid expansion. Expansion tends to diminish the spatial curvature, just as blowing up a balloon makes its surface appear flatter. The enormous expansion associated with inflation means that the universe we see today began from a very tiny region of space that could have been smooth before inflation. While inflation cannot completely eliminate the dependence of the state of the universe today upon its initial state, it does greatly lessen that dependence.

Inflation theory is more plausible, and exciting, because it can be grounded in particle physics ideas about unification and symmetry breaking. The unified theories require the existence of condensates, whose space-filling presence makes the symmetry of the fundamental equations less manifest but more consistent with observation. As described in the section "Unification and the Identity of the Dark Matter" in Chapter 3, the phenomenon is known to occur in the weak interaction. It also occurs (in a somewhat different way) in the strong interaction, in the theory of superconductivity, and in many other examples in the physics of materials. It is not an extravagant novelty.

In all physical examples of condensates, when the temperature is raised sufficiently the condensate evaporates or melts away. (Such a phase transition occurs when ice melts to become water.) The laws of physics at the higher temperature look quite different—they have more symmetry. Another example may be useful. In an ordinary magnet, the spins of the atoms are aligned at low temperatures because the total energy of the system is lower in such a configuration. This alignment obscures the isotropy of space by making it appear that there is a preferred direction (the direction in which the spins are aligned). At high temperatures, the energy advantage associated with aligned spins is no longer important, the spins of the individual atoms are no longer aligned, and the isotropy of space is no longer obscured (the broken symmetry at low temperatures is restored at high temperatures).

In a cosmological context, the consequences of a phase transition can be dramatic. At high temperature, before the condensate settles down to its equilibrium, or vacuum, value (its "frozen" state, to continue the aqueous analogy), a great deal of energy is present in the system. That energy is in a very unusual form—not as particle mass or motion but as field energy, or false vacuum energy. False vacuum energy has quite different gravitational properties from other forms of energy. It turns out that if a large amount of vacuum energy is dissipated only slowly, it causes a period of inflation, of exponentially rapid expansion of the universe.

As is discussed in later chapters, observational cosmology has recently yielded powerful hints that inflation occurred. The ideas of particle physics suggest why it might have occurred. But as yet there is no single convincing, specific model for inflation. Existing models contain many arbitrary assumptions and are ad hoc. While they show that inflation has a plausible theoretical basis, they are certainly unsatisfactory in detail. Thus to understand properly this central facet of cosmology may require the development of a more complete unified theory of gravity and matter.

Another simple yet profound property of the known universe is that it is made of matter rather than antimatter. More specifically, distant stars and galaxies are all made out of protons and neutrons, while antiprotons and antineutrons are very rare in the universe. In the Standard Model, at low temperature, the number of protons minus antiprotons (or, to be more precise, the number of quarks minus antiquarks) cannot change. If that were the whole story, the asymmetry between matter and antimatter would simply be an initial condition from the big bang, locked in for all time. There would be no deeper explanation of it, nor any deduction of its magnitude from the laws of physics. But the unified theories, as discussed above, include interactions that change quarks into antiquarks (or other particles). Thus the number of quarks minus antiquarks is not frozen in; rather, it can evolve with time. Indeed, if any such processes occur, then at sufficiently high temperature symmetry will be restored, and there will be equal numbers of quarks and antiquarks. The present-day universe, where matter dominates antimatter, must have evolved from past equality.

So the stage is set for a dynamical calculation of the universal difference between quark and antiquark densities. Many models have been considered. With some assumptions, it is possible to achieve agreement with observation, although not with the Standard Model alone. As was the case for inflation, in order to develop a proper, convincing theory of matter-antimatter asymmetry, physicists need a deeper theory.

Particle Candidates for Dark Matter and the Mystery of Dark Energy

Perhaps the most tangible hint for new physics from cosmology is the problem of dark matter. A wide variety of astronomical measurements indicate that the universe contains considerably more matter than can be accounted for by ordinary matter in all forms (e.g., stars, gas, and black holes). This additional mass (dark matter) is not seen directly but rather through the effect of its gravity on the motion or the light of visible objects.

Here arises a truly extraordinary opportunity for discovery—what is this stuff that makes up most of the universe by weight? To heighten the tension, developments in particle physics suggest two quite specific, very plausible candidate particles. Indeed, each of these candidates was proposed for theoretical reasons unrelated to the dark mass problem, and only later was their potential to solve this problem realized.

One candidate arises from the idea of supersymmetry. This hypothetical extension of the Standard Model is introduced in Chapter 3, in the section "Unification and the Identity of Dark Matter." It postulates a doubling in the number of fundamental particles, pairing each known particle with an as yet unseen "superpartner" particle. One of these is a light, stable, neutral fermion called the neutralino. This is a leading candidate for a major component of the dark matter.

The other leading candidate is a hypothetical particle called the axion. It appears as a consequence of theoretical extensions introduced to solve a quite different problem in the foundations of the Standard Model. The axion is a very light particle but could have been produced very copiously during the big bang. The special detectors needed to search for axions are very different in detail from those that can search for neutralinos. But, as in the neutralino case, first-generation experiments exist, and improvements to reach the needed sensitivity are feasible.

Finally, the most intriguing and most recent hint for new physics from cosmology is the observation that the expansion of the universe is speeding up, rather than slowing down. If correct, this indicates the presence of a mysterious energy form—dark energy—that pervades the universe with a gravitational effect that is repulsive rather than attractive. While particle physics has had much to say about dark matter, thus far it has shed little or no light on dark energy. Nonetheless, it seems clear that a fundamental understanding of this new form of energy will require new physics. Dark energy and dark matter are discussed at greater length in Chapter 5.

Theoretical Questions and Insights

Theoretical physicists have long sought to extend the range of applicability of their theories, synthesize the explanations of diverse physical phenomena, and unify the underlying principles. After the towering achievements of the last century, briefly reviewed in the previous sections, there is better material to work with than ever before—a remarkably detailed, specific, and powerful theory of matter, and a beautiful, fruitful theory of space-time. Can they be joined together? There are good reasons to be optimistic.

This discussion has reviewed how the unification of interaction strengths could arise, despite their different observed values, as a result of the effects of quantum corrections. The underlying equality of the strong, weak, and electromagnetic couplings emerges only when they are extrapolated to very high energy. Extending this calculation to include the gravitational coupling as well yields a delightful surprise: The extrapolated gravitational coupling meets the others, at nearly the same high energy (see Figure 2.4)! Is nature hinting at unification of all forces?

The most ambitious and impressive attempts to construct a unified space-time-matter theory involve an evolving set of ideas known variously as string theory, superstring theory, or M theory. Here the term "string theory" is used to denote the entire complex of ideas. String theory is not yet fully developed; so far, no specific predictions about the physical world have emerged. But even the current partial understanding suggests to many physicists that string theory may be on the right track. This report is not able to do justice to what has become a large and mathematically sophisticated body of work; it confines itself to a few brief indications.

String theory takes as its starting point the problem of constructing a consistent quantum theory of strings (as the progenitors of "elementary" particles). Remarkably, this theory predicts the existence of gravity. Moreover, the resulting theory of gravity, unlike conventional general relativity, does not suffer from the problem of infinite quantum corrections. Further, it appears that string theory avoids the apparent paradox associated with Hawking radiation, by showing that the radiation emitted from black holes is not at all random. Thus string theory offers the only known solution to two major theoretical problems that emerge when quantum mechanics is applied to gravity. Clearly, this is a direction to be pursued.

String theory is most naturally formulated in 10 or 11 space-time dimensions; it cannot be made consistent using only the observed 4. In constructing models of the physical world one must assume that most of these dimensions somehow curl up, leaving the familiar 4 (3 space, 1 time) extended dimensions. At first this may sound artificial, but many solutions of the theory having this behavior are known. Some even contain particles and interactions that broadly resemble the Standard Model, and they can incorporate low-energy supersymmetry, unification of couplings, and axions. Unfortunately there are also apparently equally valid solutions that do not have these features. No completely satisfactory theoretical reason for preferring one model to another has yet emerged. Nor is any single known solution empirically satisfactory in all respects.

A key feature of string theory is supersymmetry, the symmetry that relates matter particles and the force carriers (see Box 2.4). While many aspects of string theory do not easily lend themselves to testing, supersymmetry's prediction of the doubling of the number of elementary particles is imminently testable and the quest of the next generation of particle accelerators.

Finally, any theory of space-time-matter must address what seems at present to be the most profoundly mysterious question in physical science. Researchers know that the vacuum state is anything but trivial: it is populated with virtual particles and symmetry-breaking condensates. One might think all this structure would contain energy. The definition of zero energy can be arbitrarily adjusted in many theories, but once the adjustment is made in one epoch of the universe it cannot be altered. One would therefore expect the effects of quantum corrections to give a vacuum energy in all epochs. Indeed, as argued above, this can account for the early inflationary epoch. Straightforward estimates of the expected scale of this energy in the present epoch give values far in excess of what is allowed experimentally. This is called the problem of the cosmological constant, because the mathematical description of the energy of the vacuum is equivalent to the cosmological constant originally introduced by Einstein to keep the universe from expanding or contracting. The discrepancy, depending on how the estimates are made, is at least a factor of 10^{55}, and indicates a major gap in understanding of the vacuum and gravity.

Until very recently, it seemed reasonable to hope that some yet-undiscovered symmetry would require that all the sources of energy must cancel, so that empty space would have exactly zero energy today. But recent measurements indicate that the energy of the vacuum, while absurdly small compared with the theoretical estimates mentioned above, is not zero (see Chapter 4). Indeed, it seems to contribute about twice as much to the average energy density of the universe as all matter (ordinary plus "dark"). For the other problems mentioned here, physicists have identified some very promising lines of attack. But for the cosmological constant problem, some fundamentally new idea seems required.

Many of the challenging questions today could not even be formulated only a few years ago. The experimental and observational data and techniques at hand today are beginning to provide access to information directly relevant to our questions. Rapid progress toward better data can be anticipated. It is an exciting time for this area of science, which has blossomed through the overlapping interests of physics and astronomy.

3

How Are Matter, Space, and Time Unified?

Physicists have long believed that a fundamental, encompassing theory of matter, space, and time must be attainable. The remarkable progress described in Chapter 2 suggests that the opportunity to achieve that unification may be at hand. Realizing that opportunity will involve obtaining information both from high-energy physics laboratory and accelerator experiments and from observations in astronomy and cosmology. This chapter explores the open questions and opportunities for progress in the coming years in exploring the implications of physics beyond the Standard Model for the early universe. Further, it addresses opportunities to use particles from sources outside Earth to reveal physics beyond the Standard Model.

The earliest history of the universe is dominated by physics of the highest energies, so that gaining an understanding of it depends on progress in understanding microscopic physics in these extreme domains. Conversely, the universe, unlike accelerators where experiments are limited by available beam lines and interaction regions, is an ever-open laboratory, one that produces a great range of phenomena that span an incredible energy range and that can be used to probe and extend ideas on microphysics. Some important relics that could have been produced only at these early times may remain today. Astronomical and astrophysical studies add immeasurably and often uniquely to important aspects of particle physics beyond the Standard Model, addressing questions such as these: Do protons decay? Do neutrinos have mass? Is nature supersymmetric? What constitutes the dark energy? Are there additional dimensions of space beyond the familiar three?

The triumph of the Standard Model is based largely on data from particle accelerators of ever-increasing energies, constructed over the past 50 years. Without the Standard Model, it would have been impossible to make with any confidence the very large extrapolations in energy that have yielded insights into the conditions of the early universe.

What can be expected from accelerator-based facilities, the center of the traditional high-energy physics effort? The search for the Higgs boson and for supersymmetric partners of the known particles is a primary focus of the programs at the highest-energy accelerators, such as at the Tevatron at Fermilab and the Large Hadron Collider (LHC) at CERN and even at the next large accelerator to be built after the LHC, which will be designed to perform incisive studies of these particles' properties.

Accelerator experiments permit irreplaceable measurements for exploring the Standard Model and beyond, including studies of neutrino masses and the violation charge-parity (CP) symmetry (see Chapter 5, section "Dark Energy"), as well as the creation of an exotic form of matter known as the quark-gluon plasma to mimic an important phase in the early universe. Accelerators are also capable of seeing manifestations of extra dimensions that are macroscopic. This possibility, a recent speculation from string theory, has profound implications for understanding the physics of the very early universe. Experimental signatures include the apparent loss of energy in particle interactions, which, in fact, has gone off into the additional dimensions. Experiments at the Tevatron and the LHC should have significant sensitivity to this exciting possibility.

Rather than address ongoing and proposed accelerator programs that are reviewed elsewhere by other responsible scientific groups (laboratory program committees, the NRC, and the DOE/NSF High Energy Physics Advisory Panel and the Nuclear Science Advisory Committee), this committee focuses on identifying additional and complementary opportunities for the use of new techniques and technologies to probe the most fundamental questions at the interface between particle physics and astronomy and astrophysics. This chapter discusses, in turn, experiments seeking signatures of unification, identifying the dark matter, and probing the very foundations of our science.

LOOKING FOR SIGNATURES OF UNIFICATION

The hypothesis that a single unified theory can account for the three separate forces of the Standard Model is attractive in many ways. Such a theory would organize the quarks and leptons into a simple, beautiful structure and would explain the patterns of charges, which otherwise seem quite arbitrary. And most impressively, by including low-energy supersymmetry, it would account quantitatively for the relative values of the different observed coupling strengths.

Unified theories predict additional effects that go beyond the Standard Model. In the following subsections the most promising of these new phenomena are discussed.

Proton Decay

A great cosmological question is how the current preponderance of matter over antimatter in the universe came about. Presumably the abundances of both were equal immediately after the big bang, just as the numbers of negative and positive charges were equal. The subsequent interactions that established the matter-antimatter imbalance at very high energies must also allow proton decay, although at a very low rate given the low energy (mass) of the proton.

Unified theories predict that protons are unstable. Early estimates based on the simplest unified theories suggested lifetimes on the order of 10^{30} years. But those predictions were discounted with the first round of experiments. Today, the predicted lifetime of protons is on the order of 10^{35} years or less in the most viable models. Experiments currently set lower limits (depending on the mode of decay) of roughly 10^{32} to 10^{33} years.

Because it would imply the instability of all nuclear matter, the discovery of proton decay would be a historic event that provides a unique window onto some of the most fundamental questions in physics and cosmology. Different unified models make different predictions for the most likely modes of proton decay. Models with supersymmetry, for example, favor decays that include K mesons and neutrinos.

Much effort has already been devoted to the search for proton decay, the principal original goal of the Kamiokande and Super-Kamiokande detectors in Japan, the Frejus experiment in Europe, and the Irvine-Michigan-Brookhaven (IMB) and Soudan detectors in the United States. Although no protons were observed to decay in these experiments, the scientists working there made impressive discoveries in neutrino physics. Furthermore, these experiments allowed limits to be defined on proton decay that already rule out the simplest grand unified theories.

Clearly, achieving substantial improvements in experimental sensitivity to proton decay will be important to improving our understanding of the early universe. As a bonus, such experiments could also accommodate an extensive neutrino physics program including the study of neutrino properties by detecting neutrino beams from distant accelerators and supernovae in our galaxy and nearby galaxies.

Neutrino Masses and Neutrino Oscillations

As far as physicists know, neutrinos interact only by the weak force, passing through Earth, for example, with ease. Until recently, it was widely believed that neutrinos were also massless, like photons. Despite having properties that render them very elusive, neutrinos can be and have been studied extensively in particle accelerators and nuclear reactors, and they can have major consequences in the cosmos.

For example, even though they interact extraordinarily weakly, there was a time in the early universe when even neutrinos were in thermal equilibrium with the high-density, seething plasma of particles and force carriers. At about 1 second after the big bang, the universe became too diffuse to maintain that equilibrium, and neutrinos were free to expand and cool just as the photons of the microwave background did 400,000 years later. Created in numbers comparable to the number of photons (and a billionfold more abundant than protons), neutrinos with a small but non-zero mass of only a few eV/c^2 (electron-volts divided by the speed of light squared; in this unit, the electron mass is 511,000) would contribute a significant fraction of the dark matter (though still not enough to allow them to be the seeds of galactic and large-scale structure formation). Neutrinos from weak processes that power the Sun and neutrinos generated in the atmosphere from the decay of secondary particles produced by cosmic rays are providing key information about these elusive particles and their role in the cosmos. A burst of neutrinos was detected on Earth from the explosion of supernova SN1987A, broadly confirming the predictions of supernova models and opening up an astronomical window for the study of a variety of effects beyond the Standard Model. No experiment has directly detected the cosmic neutrino background, but it is likely that the effects of even a 1 eV/c^2 neutrino on structure formation could be seen indirectly by its imprint on the large-scale distribution of matter in the universe. The Sloan Digital Sky Survey, a map of the universe being made from the positions of 1 million galaxies, will soon enable detecting the effect of neutrinos on large-scale structure.

In the early universe, neutrinos played a critical role in the formation of elements beyond hydrogen through their ability to transform protons into neutrons and vice versa. The particular pattern of abundances of hydrogen, helium, and lithium nuclei produced depends critically on the rates of neutron production, capture, and decay, which in turn depend on the nature and properties of neutrinos. The predicted abundances have been confirmed spectacularly in studies of the abundances of these elements today.

We know that there are only three light neutrino types (also called "fla-vors")—the electron neutrino, the muon neutrino, and the tau neutrino—named for the particles into which they are transmuted by emission or absorption of a W boson (recall Figure 2.1). The concordance between the predicted and observed cosmic abundances of the light elements would not be nearly as good were there more than these three flavors of neutrinos, and this result from cosmology gave an important early constraint on the num-ber of neutrinos. Subsequently, the number of neutrino flavors was very accurately measured by experiments at the Stanford Linear Accelerator Cen-ter's Linear Collider and CERN's Large Electron-Positron Collider (LEP).

Within the Standard Model, the total number of electron neutrinos and electrons minus the total number of electron antineutrinos and positrons in the universe never changes. Similar lepton-family-number conservation laws apply to the mu and tau families as well. However, physicists have long been alert to the possibility that the lepton-number conservation laws may be only approximate. Indeed, this may be suggested by the fact that similar laws for the conservation of different quark types are known to be only approximate. In a unified theory, it would be natural for quarks and leptons to appear on an equal footing, compelling researchers to think that the conservation of lepton-number really will be violated.

A subtle phenomenon that can cause lepton-family-number violation is neutrino oscillation: One flavor of neutrino produced initially may be de-tected later as another flavor, with a probability that changes as the neutrino moves through space or passes through matter (see diagram in Figure 3.1a and 3.1b). The changes are oscillatory in the sense that the probability of a change in flavor occurring reaches a maximum at a certain distance, dimin-ishes to zero at twice that distance, and so on. The effect can occur only if different neutrinos have different masses. The rate of oscillation depends on the energy of the neutrino, on the mass differences between the various neutrinos, and on the value of a "mixing factor" that controls the process of conversion from one to the other. If the mass differences are tiny, then sensitivity to neutrino oscillations can be achieved only by looking at neu-trinos that have traveled a very long distance, since the oscillations are then very gradual, although the oscillation rate can be enhanced for electron-type neutrinos traveling through dense matter, for example in the Sun.

The first real hints that neutrinos oscillate came from studies of solar neutrinos. The nuclear reactions that power the Sun produce electron neu-trinos. Because they interact so weakly, these neutrinos from the Sun can be detected only in experiments on a heroic scale. For many years the only suitable detector was a gigantic vat of cleaning fluid, mounted and

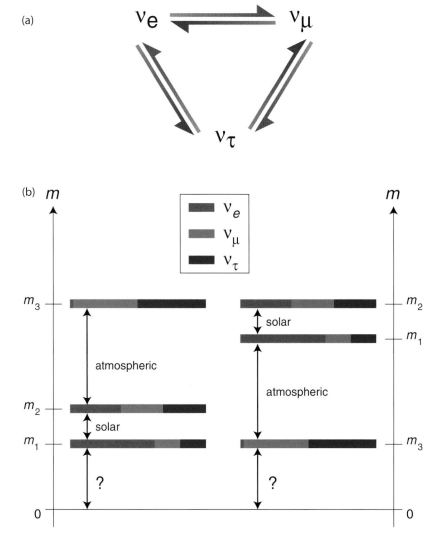

FIGURE 3.1   (a) If neutrinos have mass, the different types mix with one another, as indicated in the first diagram. The so-called neutrino mixing parameters correspond to the arrows in each direction. It is because of this mixing that one flavor of neutrino can "disappear" (and reappear as a another flavor that has different detailed interactions) and be noted as a deficit in the detector. (b) Two mass schemes for neutrinos are consistent with measurements of atmospheric and solar neutrinos. The three "mass states" are mixtures of the different neutrino types, as illustrated in the second figure. Note, too, that the solar and atmospheric neutrino experiments determine mass differences and do not set the absolute scale of neutrino masses. Image courtesy of H. Murayama, University of California at Berkeley.

instrumented by Ray Davis in the Homestake Mine in South Dakota. Davis succeeded in observing electron neutrinos, but at roughly one-third the expected rate. Several later experiments have confirmed this deficit by looking at lower-energy neutrinos, whose rate prediction is less sensitive to details of the model of the Sun. The leading interpretation of these observations is that electron neutrinos emitted from the Sun have partially oscillated into muon or tau neutrinos that cannot be detected using the experiments designed by Davis and his successors.

Recent dramatic experimental developments in neutrino oscillations have emerged from the study of neutrinos originating in the atmosphere as by-products of cosmic ray interactions. Since cosmic rays have been carefully studied for many decades, it is possible to predict with considerable confidence the expected relative abundance of the different types of neutrinos so produced. The experiments designed to search for proton decay, the Irvine-Michigan-Brookhaven (IMB) and Kamiokande experiments, observed that the ratio of the number of muon neutrinos to electron neutrinos fell below theoretical expectations. The ratio, naively expected to be 2 (twice as many muon neutrinos as electron neutrinos come from pion decay) is calculable to an accuracy of about 5 percent. It was found to be low by about 40 percent.

A recent development, from the Super-Kamiokande detector in Japan (see Figure 3.2), is the observation that the ratio of muon to electron neutrinos depends on the distance that these neutrinos have traveled since their creation. Researchers at Super-Kamiokande see this effect as a modulation of the flux of muon neutrinos as a function of the angle in the sky at which they originate. Muon neutrinos created in Earth's atmosphere and arriving at the Super-Kamiokande detector having traveled through the Earth's mass are detected at about one half the rate of those created in the atmosphere directly above the detector. Observation of this dependence on distance from point of creation strongly suggests that the muon neutrinos have oscillated, and, since there is no corresponding angular dependence in the flux of electron neutrinos, the oscillation most likely involves another neutrino, such as the tau neutrino. Even more recently, the Sudbury Neutrino Observatory in Canada (see Figure 3.3) has confirmed that electron-type neutrinos are less than half of the total number of solar neutrinos reaching Earth.

Solar neutrino experiments have recently given added evidence for electron neutrino oscillation. The early results giving less-than-expected electron-neutrino flux from the Sun have been confirmed. The Sudbury Neutrino Observatory detector has given an accurate measurement of the electron neutrino flux. The Super-Kamiokande detector in Japan observes a

FIGURE 3.2   The Super-Kamiokande detector. Here, scientists (in a rubber raft) inspect the large photomultiplier tubes as the enormous tank is filled with water. Image courtesy of the Institute for Cosmic Ray Research, University of Tokyo.

FIGURE 3.3   The Sudbury Neutrino Observatory (SNO). SNO consists of 1,000 tons of heavy water (made of deuterium and oxygen rather than hydrogen and oxygen) contained in an acrylic vessel (viewed here with a fisheye lens) and surrounded by 9,500 photomultiplier tubes. Neutrino interactions with heavy water reveal separately the number of electron neutrinos and other types. Image courtesy of Lawrence Berkeley National Laboratory.

larger total flux, but this detector is sensitive at different levels to all types of neutrinos. The comparison of the two results thus gives a clear indication that neutrinos produced in the Sun as electron-type arrive at Earth as a mixture containing other types, showing that neutrinos have mass and that neutrino oscillation occurs. The combination of the solar and atmospheric results indicates that the mixing angles that characterize the defined-mass neutrinos in terms of the defined-flavor species have a pattern quite different from the equivalent matrix for quarks.

Since the initial experiment of Clyde Cowan and Frederick Reines that discovered the neutrino in 1957, reactors and accelerators have been a mainstay of research into neutrino properties. An accelerator-based neutrino oscillation experiment at Los Alamos National Laboratory, Liquid Scintillator Neutrino Detector (LSND), has also found evidence for oscillation between the electron neutrino and the muon neutrino. This experiment found a difference in mass between 0.15 eV/c^2 and 1.5 eV/c^2, a much larger value than was obtained in other experiments. If there are only three neutrino types, this result and the evidence from atmospheric and solar neutrinos cannot be accommodated simultaneously. Either some additional sterile neutrino is playing a role, or one or more of the results have been misinterpreted. Only additional precise experimental tests can tell.

There is now strong evidence that neutrinos have mass. It is important to pursue these studies further. Large neutrino detectors located deep underground can study oscillations from laboratory-produced neutrino beams, as well as look for angular dependence in neutrinos from the atmosphere. These solar and atmospheric neutrino results describe neutrino *disappearance* effects, i.e., they detect a shortage of the neutrino type produced. More convincing would be an experiment in which an *appearance* effect is observed, i.e., detection of a type of neutrino not produced at the source.

Neutrino oscillation experiments measure only differences between the masses of neutrinos (more precisely, the difference between the squares of their masses), not the actual value of either mass. To determine the mass itself requires a different approach. Direct measurements are limited in precision both by technical capabilities and by the amount of the energy released in the relevant decays producing neutrinos. (The determination of their mass requires the use of low-energy neutrinos: the lower the energy, the better.) Careful studies of the end-point behavior of the spectrum of electrons from tritium beta decay could in principle yield indications of neutrino mass, but the smaller the mass, the more difficult this approach becomes.

One means of illuminating some aspects of the neutrino mass scale might be the study of a rare process in which a nucleus decays weakly with the emission of an electron and a positron but with no neutrinos. The predicted rate for this double-beta decay depends on the neutrino mass and also on the relationship of the neutrino to its antiparticle. Among the mysteries remaining to be resolved for the neutrinos, one is whether each neutrino is identical to its own antiparticle (in which case it is called a Majorana particle) or whether, like other massive fermions, such as the electron, it has a distinct antiparticle partner (a Dirac particle). Owing to the weak interaction's enforcement of opposite handedness for neutrinos and antineutrinos, most direct experimental tests of this question are impossibly difficult. But observation of neutrinoless double-beta decay would demonstrate the Majorana character of neutrinos. No signal has been seen to date for this type of decay, setting a neutrino mass limit of a few tenths of an eV, provided neutrinos are Majorana particles. New double-beta decay experiments using radioactive sources on the scale of tons will be needed to achieve a neutrino mass sensitivity in the range of 0.01 eV/c^2. This is the interesting range suggested by the neutrino-oscillation evidence described above.

Single- and double-beta decay experiments directly probe the mass of the electron neutrino. But the small mass differences that are representative of oscillations forge links among various masses. When these mass differences are known, to measure any one neutrino mass is to measure them all.

The probable values of the neutrino masses indicated by the oscillation experiments are very small, far smaller than the analogues for any other leptons or quarks. The occurrence of neutrino oscillations is the only known phenomenon in particle physics that is not accounted for by the Standard Model in its minimal form. What might this mean?

In grand unified theories, the Standard Model describes only the most accessible part of a larger theory, so it is not complete. The extra particles in a complete theory might be very heavy, so that their effects, on neutrino masses in particular, will be small. Remarkably, by analyzing these extensions of the Standard Model, theorists predicted neutrino masses of roughly the right magnitude before they were observed. Thus the recent experimental discoveries about neutrinos suggest that these bold ideas may be on the right track, and further experimental tests might help refine or refute them.

Very-High-Energy Cosmic Rays

Several serious ideas related to unification and unknown forces, including cosmic strings and dark-matter decays and annihilation (discussed below), would result in signatures in the high-energy cosmic rays detected at Earth. Gamma-ray bursts and ultrahigh-energy cosmic rays have been observed, but their origins are not well understood (see Chapter 7, sections "Understanding the Destiny of the Universe" and "Exploring the Unification of the Forces from Underground"). Further, cosmic rays provide the highest-energy particle beams observable on Earth and hence can be used to probe physics inaccessible at accelerator laboratories. Modern cosmic ray detectors, using sensitive phototubes deployed on a large scale, measure the huge, energetic showers created by very-high-energy primary particles either at Earth's surface or in the atmosphere. The same technologies can be applied on a much larger scale. Space-based versions of such detectors have been proposed.

UNIFICATION AND THE IDENTITY OF DARK MATTER

The amount of matter in the universe is an essential cosmological parameter. Evidence has accumulated for the existence of a large amount of exotic "dark matter"—almost 10 times the amount of ordinary matter (see

Chapter 5). According to the current paradigm for structure formation in the universe, ordinary matter falls into clumps of dark matter. The dark matter has been detected through its gravitational effect on the motion of stars and, more recently, through its gravitational lensing of light from more distant galaxies. This matter, whatever it is, interacts very weakly with photons.

A major puzzle is what dark matter is made of. Neutrinos are the only candidate of all the known particles. But they cannot constitute all of the dark matter; with their small masses and velocities near the speed of light, they would not have been gravitationally trapped in density fluctuations in the early universe. Alternative candidates are needed to account for the "cold" (i.e., massive, slowly moving) dark matter that seems to govern structure formation. Remarkably, some compelling ideas in particle physics both predict the existence of particles that could make up this dark matter and suggest ways of detecting them.

The simplest implementations of supersymmetry suggest a new, electrically neutral, stable particle type that interacts very weakly—the neutralino. It is thought to have a mass in the range of 100 GeV/c^2. Despite varying estimates of the neutralino's abundance from production in the early stages of the big bang, the amount required for dark matter is easily accommodated. Several promising ways to look for neutralinos are discussed in Chapter 5.

Another hypothetical particle that could be a significant component of dark matter is the axion, which was introduced into particle physics to solve a deficiency in the Standard Model. Although the Standard Model is generally a reliable guide to the interactions that can occur in nature, it fails to explain why the strong force does not violate matter-antimatter symmetry, technically known as charge-parity (CP) symmetry. One suggestion introduces an additional, but slightly broken symmetry, into the theory; a general consequence of adding such a symmetry is the prediction of an additional low-mass and very weakly interacting particle, the axion.

Fortunately, the idea of an axion is testable. If axions exist, they would have been produced abundantly during the big bang and could quite naturally provide the required dark matter. It is possible to carry out an experiment sensitive to the cosmic axion background using large electromagnetic cavities embedded in strong magnetic fields (see Chapter 5).

Many additional dark matter candidates are suggested by other theories (some more speculative than others), but the neutralino and the axion stand out because they are motivated by important concepts in particle physics, and their properties are well characterized and predictable.

EXAMINING THE FOUNDATIONS OF UNIFICATION

Searching for Violation of Basic Symmetries

The universe around us is made of matter, not antimatter. To explain the observed difference in the amounts of antimatter and matter seen today requires, in addition to the baryon-number changing processes discussed above in this chapter, violation of CP symmetry.

There are well-established laboratory manifestations of CP violation, seen in the decays of the neutral K meson, or kaon. But very little is known about the fundamental nature of this important phenomenon. Is the pattern of CP violation consistent with that of the Standard Model of particle physics? The search for new sources of CP violation is important. It appears that there must be at least one new source since the magnitude of the CP violation allowed by the Standard Model appears to be far smaller than that needed in the very early universe to account for the dominance of matter over antimatter. Evidence of CP violation in the neutrino sector could lead to a quite different model for the development of the matter-antimatter asymmetry of the present universe. There is much still to be learned in this area.

Important new studies of CP nonconservation in B decays have recently yielded first results, showing a definite CP-violating effect in one channel, consistent with that predicted by the Standard Model. An ongoing program studying the many additional modes is needed, as are additional experiments sensitive to other B decays or to very rare kaon decays.

Some of the hypothesized sources of CP violation beyond the Standard Model predict electric dipole moments of elementary particles such as the neutron and the electron, which could one day be detectable in ambitious experiments. (A symmetry principle called time-reversal invariance, or T symmetry, holds that the laws of physics should be the same when time is run backwards. An electric dipole moment would be a violation of T symmetry.) Many unification models, especially those incorporating low-energy supersymmetry, predict an additional and quite different sort of T violation that could be visible through its very tiny effects on ordinary matter. In response to an applied electric field, the macroscopic material would generate, by T violation, a small magnetic field (or, conversely, an applied magnetic field could generate a small electric field). Modern precision spectroscopic techniques provide sensitive tools with which to look for such effects.

In all field theories, T violation and CP violation are intimately connected, since such theories incorporate an overall prediction of a combined CPT symmetry that must be exact. However, the higher the energy, the less string theory looks like a field theory. Thus, the search for violations of CPT symmetry is a potential test for the validity of string theory.

Probing Unification with Gravitation Experiments

After more than 300 years, Newton's law of gravitation remains experimentally valid in and around Earth (at least up to the tiny corrections resulting from general relativity). It states that the net force between two uncharged objects is proportional to mass and independent of internal composition (the equivalence principle) and decreases as the inverse square of the separation. Strangely, high-precision tests of Newton's basic law on laboratory scales may provide important probes of unification.

The axion is but one of several hypothetical very light, very weakly coupled particles suggested to resolve issues in particle physics. Others are familons, dilatons, and moduli fields. (A proper explanation of these possibilities would take this discussion far afield.) One way to be sensitive to light particles such as the axion is to detect the forces they generate. Since an inverse relationship exists between the mass of a particle and the range of the associated force, such light particles could generate new forces on macroscopic scales of microns and larger. These forces would appear as deviations from Newton's inverse-square law of gravity. Also, since these putative particles could interact differently with different kinds of material, they could result in testable violations of the principle of equivalence. The violation of the equivalence principle is a generic prediction of string theory, although the level of the violation is not currently predictable.

To address the speculation that nature contains extra spatial dimensions, possibly some of macroscopic size, it is necessary to explain why we experience only three spatial dimensions. According to one explanation, the ordinary particles we are made of are confined to three-dimensional structures ("branes") that exist within the larger space, while the graviton is not so confined. This arrangement would also modify the behavior of the gravitational force at distances comparable to the size of the extra dimension.

Discovery of deviations from Newton's gravity at any distance scale would revolutionize knowledge of the physical world. Tests of the principle of equivalence in the laboratory and using the Moon have reached the level of parts in 10^{13} and could be improved by another order of magnitude, while a space experiment could yield improvement by a factor of 10^5. At scales of 1 mm or less, sensitive laboratory inverse-square law experiments that are clever variations on the original one by Henry Cavendish are under way, with the goal of probing the force between bodies in the submillimeter range (while excluding the dominating effects of electromagnetic forces). See Figure 3.4 for an experimental design.

Are the "Constants" Constant?

Modern theories of particle physics suggest that some or all of the quantities regarded as constants of nature are in reality associated with dynamical fields that change. The axion field is an excellent example; familons, dilatons, and moduli fields are other examples. In string theory, as

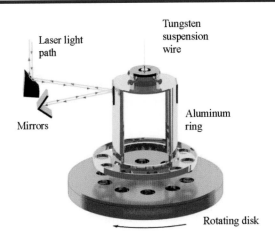

FIGURE 3.4 Extra dimensions that are open to gravitational interactions may explain gravity's apparent weakness in our four dimensions. If those dimensions are "curled up" on the scale of fractions of a millimeter, it may be possible to observe a strengthening of the gravitational force at very short distances. The highly sensitive short-range torsion balance shown here is used to detect this effect. An aluminum ring was suspended by a fine tungsten wire above a disk that rotated once every 2 hours. The ring and disk both had $10^3/_8$-inch-diameter holes bored into them. The gravitational force between the "missing mass" in the two sets of 10 holes produced a twist on the ring that varied back and forth 10 times for each revolution of the disk. The disk's twist was measured by bouncing a laser beam off one of two mirrors mounted above the ring. So far, extra dimensions of extent greater than 0.2 mm have been ruled out by experiments such as this one. Image courtesy of E. Adelberger, B. Heckel, and E. Swanson, University of Washington.

currently understood, it appears that all "constants" are in principle dynamical. Modern precision spectroscopic techniques can be used to search for the evolution of the electromagnetic coupling with great sensitivity, by looking at the spectra of distant, and hence ancient, stars.

The mass of the photon is strictly zero in the Standard Model. It is severely constrained by astronomical observations of electromagnetic fields at distances of 10^{20} meters from their source, providing an impressive limit of about 10^{-33} of the electron mass. Speculative ideas about the quantum structure of space allow the speed of light to vary with photon energy. This concept is testable by monitoring the arrival times of gamma rays of different energies in gamma-ray bursts from distant sources, probing a fundamental property of light in a new regime.

Monitoring the arrival times of neutrinos from astrophysical sources such as supernovae also provides a means of directly probing neutrino masses (especially those of muon and tau neutrinos, which are much less accessible in the laboratory). Unfortunately, supernovae are rare events, one per 30 years or so within our galaxy, so such measurements cannot be scheduled; rather, experiments must be prepared to catch a supernova whenever it happens.

NEW OPPORTUNITIES

All of the research fields discussed above span, in one way or another, the boundary between particle physics and the physics of the universe. In recent years it has been the physics at this boundary that presents and probes ideas at the limits of the knowledge of matter and of space-time. It will take the concerted efforts of astrophysicists and particle physicists to mine this rich area for all that can be learned from it. The discussion in this chapter can be summarized by posing four of the crosscutting fundamental science questions for the new century outlined in this report.

Are Protons Unstable?

The discovery of proton decay and improved understanding of CP violation would provide evidence for unification and help to answer the question of why matter in the universe dominates antimatter. Large-volume detectors with greater sensitivity could dramatically improve limits on the proton lifetime, and further laboratory and accelerator tests of CP violation could distinguish among competing models of unification.

What Are the Masses of the Neutrinos?

There is strong evidence that neutrinos have a mass and that oscillations occur among the various neutrino flavors. Several opportunities are ripe for experimental progress. The needed measurements or observations include confirming various effects of neutrino oscillations and identifying the neutrino species involved in each, measuring the values of the mixing parameters responsible for the observed solar neutrino abundances, and measuring the values of the neutrino masses themselves. Answers to these problems are within reach. Much more difficult and subtle issues remain, such as the particle-antiparticle properties of neutrinos and possible CP-symmetry violations in their transitions. New global-scale investigations in the planning stages should culminate in precise results describing these elusive fundamental particles.

What Is Dark Matter?

Well-founded ideas from unification and particle physics suggest interesting candidates for dark matter, such as neutralinos and axions, with calculable properties. Do these particles exist? Are any of them the actual dark matter observed astronomically? Initial experiments to detect these particles have been mounted, but more sensitivite searches will be needed to detect or rule out these candidates.

Are There Extra Dimensions?

Attempts to unify space, time, and matter beyond the Standard Model and general relativity introduce additional interactions and extra space-time dimensions. Tests of the strength of gravity at short range, experiments at particle accelerators, and tests of the principle of equivalence can probe for such signatures of unification.

4

How Did the Universe Get Going?

Over the past several decades, physicists and astronomers have constructed a remarkable paradigm, known as the big bang model, to describe the expanding universe. By combining observations of distant galaxies, the cosmic microwave background (CMB) radiation, and the abundances of the lightest elements with the fundamental theories of gravity and atomic and nuclear physics, researchers have been able to account, in large measure, for the evolution of the universe from the first few seconds until the present (see Box 4.1).

In the wake of this progress, there are new and deeper questions to be answered and mysteries to be explained: Is the universe flat in its spatial directions, and if so, why? Where did the structure around us—from individual galaxies to the great walls of galaxies—originate? What went bang and started the expansion? Surprisingly, the answers to these questions about phenomena on the largest imaginable scales may well be found in the physics of the smallest scales. This chapter describes the questions and challenges raised by the puzzle of the earliest evolution of the universe and the opportunities for providing answers.

BIG BANG COSMOLOGY: THE BASIC MODEL

Observations of the recession of distant galaxies confirm that the universe is expanding. As the universe expands, the density of both matter and radiation decreases with time. Thus, in the past, the universe was much denser and much hotter than it is today. Today, the universe is filled with the cosmic background radiation, the residual heat from the big bang, which has been cooled by the expansion of the universe. This radiation fills space; there are roughly 400 microwave background photons in each cubic centimeter of space.

BOX 4.1   WHAT WE KNOW ABOUT THE BIG BANG AND HOW WE KNOW IT

The big bang model embodies our accumulated knowledge about how the universe began and evolved to its present state. Like most scientific theories it is not static, but rather is constantly being tested and extended. Nor does it exist in a vacuum—its foundation being Einstein's theory of general relativity.

Testing the big bang model (or any theory) requires a theoretical framework—in this case, general relativity. If the predictions of the big bang model agree with the data, then both the big bang model and general relativity are being tested (a failure of either one would lead to discrepancies). The fundamental set of observations that support the big bang model are the expansion of the universe; the existence of the cosmic microwave background (CMB) radiation; the 0.001 percent variations in the intensity of the CMB that reflect the primeval lumpiness in the distribution of matter, which seeded all the structure seen today; and the abundance pattern of the lightest elements (hydrogen, deuterium, helium, and lithium) seen in the most primitive samples of the cosmos. A large number of other observations are also consistent with the big bang model.

Within the context of the big bang model, parameters that describe the key features of our universe are measurable. There has been great progress in recent years in improving the precision of these measurements: the temperature of the CMB has been measured to four digits, $T = 2.725$ K; the expansion rate of the universe (or Hubble constant) has been determined to a precision of 10 percent, $H_0 = 63$ to 77 km/sec/Mpc; the time back to the big bang has been determined to a precision of about 15 percent, $t = 11.5$ billion to 14.5 billion years; the average density of matter and energy has been measured and found to be between 95 and 125 percent of the critical density; independently, space has been shown to be uncurved ("flat") to a precision of about 4 percent; and the rate of change in the expansion rate has been measured, indicating that the expansion seems to be speeding up, not slowing down.

Some of these measurements require further assumptions or information beyond the assumption of general relativity; for example, to determine the time back to the big bang requires both the Hubble constant and knowledge about the matter and energy makeup of the universe. The curvature of space was determined from measurements of the size of hot and cold spots on the microwave sky and involves a minor, but nonetheless additional, assumption about the nature of the lumpiness in the distribution of matter. Some of the cosmological parameters test the basic consistency of the framework; for example, the time back to the big bang can be compared to the age of the oldest stars, between 10 billion and 14 billion years. Within the margin of error the universe is older than the oldest objects within it.

Our present understanding of the big bang takes us back to a time when the universe was a soup of elementary particles, a few microseconds after the big bang. Current attempts to extend the big bang model, such as inflation, aspire to describe even earlier moments in the universe and to answer deeper questions, such as, How did the lumpiness arise? What made the universe flat? What

(continued on next page)

BOX 4.1 *(continued)*

was the dynamite behind the big bang? The key idea of inflation is a tremendous growth spurt that occurred during the earliest moments and was caused by physics that is not yet well understood, but whose basic consequences are quite clear. They include the prediction that the universe is flat, and that the lumpiness arose from quantum fluctuations and the existence of a background of gravity waves. Testing these basic predictions tests the inflationary framework. If inflation passes these tests, and the early signs (e.g., the flatness of the universe) are that it will, then more detailed aspects of its predictions can be addressed and can lead to an understanding of

the underlying cause of inflation. The array of tests awaiting inflation is quite elaborate. For example, its prediction about the lumpiness in the distribution of matter leads to a detailed statistical description of how structure forms, once the nature of the dark matter is specified. The evidence points to the dark matter consisting of slowly moving particles (cold dark matter), and the cold dark matter scenario opens inflation to a whole array of new tests.

There is no doubt that inflation, even if correct in broad outline, will not be the last word on our understanding of the origin of the universe.

Looking outward in space is equivalent to looking backward in time. When they observe the nearby Andromeda galaxy, astronomers are detecting photons that left that galaxy 2 million years ago. Five hundred thousand years after the beginning, the temperature of the CMB radiation was 3000 K. At that temperature, hydrogen, the dominant atomic component of the universe, was ionized and existed as free protons and electrons. While cosmic background photons move freely through neutral hydrogen, they scatter easily off electrons. Thus, observing the microwave background radiation involves detecting photons that last interacted with matter during this early epoch, when the matter was mostly ionized, and provides a snapshot of the infant universe.

NASA's Cosmic Background Explorer (COBE) satellite accurately measured the energy spectrum of this background and found that it agreed with the big bang model's prediction of a thermal spectrum to better than 1 part in 10,000. Although CMB observations are measuring the physical conditions 400,000 years after the big bang, it is possible to use the big bang model to extrapolate back to early times.

Closer to the beginning of the big bang, the universe gets hotter and denser. Three minutes after the big bang, the temperature of the background radiation was roughly 1 billion K. At these high temperatures, neutrons and protons collided and fused to form most of the deuterium and helium in the universe. The big bang theory accurately accounts for the abundance of these light elements. This success is one of the primary tests of the big bang model (see Box 4.2 for more on precision cosmology).

When the universe was younger than about 10 microseconds, neutrons and protons did not exist as such. Rather, there was a soup of their constituents, quarks and gluons. One of the scientific goals of the relativistic heavy ion collider at Brookhaven National Laboratory is to confirm that at sufficiently high temperatures matter exists as a quark-gluon plasma.

At 10 micro-microseconds after the big bang, the temperature of the universe was roughly comparable to the highest energies that are now achievable at the largest particle accelerators. At these high temperatures, electrons and positrons (electrons' antiparticles) collided to produce a vast cornucopia of particles. Most of these particles did not survive to the present: They were destroyed through either annihilation or decay. However, the electron, the neutrino, and the proton may not be the only survivors. Some theories of particle physics predict that there may be other stable particles, such as axions and neutralinos (see Chapter 4, section "Refining the Big Bang: The Inflationary Paradigm"). If these exist, then they would have been created in this powerful cosmological accelerator and would have survived today as fossil relics of the earliest moments.

Moreover, as Chapter 3 points out, astronomical evidence actually suggests the existence of some new kind of particle. Since the 1970s, astronomers have known that the mass in galaxies, inferred through its gravitational influence on motions within the galaxies, vastly exceeds the mass in visible stars. Over the past two decades, they have eliminated all of the usual suspects: low-mass stars, clouds of molecular or ionized gas, massive planets, and even supermassive black holes. These particles, products of the first microsecond of the big bang, may account for the bulk of the matter in the universe and may even be detectable in laboratory and astronomical searches (see Chapters 3 and 5).

REFINING THE BIG BANG: THE INFLATIONARY PARADIGM

Despite its successes in explaining the expansion of the universe, the abundance of light elements, and the properties of the CMB, the big bang model is incomplete. It does not explain why the universe is so large and so uniform. It requires that physically disconnected regions of space all simultaneously start expanding at the same moment and at the same rate. At the beginning of this expansion, the kinetic energy of the expansion must have nearly perfectly balanced the gravitational energy counteracting the expansion. Without this nearly perfect balance, the universe would either have

BOX 4.2   PRECISION COSMOLOGY

We stand at the brink of a new era of exploration in cosmology and particle physics. The coming years will witness multiple probes of the deep relationship between physics at the highest energies and the details of the early universe and dark matter and dark energy. What are the dark matter and dark energy, and how are they related to the physics of the hot early universe? Thanks to new tools, scientists are now entering the age of precision cosmology, a phrase that only a decade ago would have been considered an oxymoron.

The new tools include measurements of the cosmic microwave background to microkelvin accuracy; redshift surveys that include samples as large as 1 million galaxies; x-ray instruments with the spatial resolution of the Hubble Space Telescope (Chandra X-ray Observatory) and spectral resolution matching that of the best optical instruments (XMM-Newton); new specialized detectors to search for dark matter particles; and in the coming years even more powerful probes.

Taken together, observations of the effects of dark matter and dark energy and of the fluctuations in the remnant radiation from the big bang will soon allow percent-level determinations of several cosmological parameters—the expansion rate (Hubble constant), the density of ordinary matter, and the curvature of space—testing the foundations of current understanding of the universe as well as the framework of general relativity itself.

The highest energies characterizing the frontier of particle physics, unattainable in any conceivable accelerator on Earth, are reached in the big bang. Perhaps some day the remnant cosmic gravitational-wave noise from the turbulent first moments will be detected. It is already possible to map the small (30 microkelvin) temperature variations in the remnant microwave radiation from the fireball that was our observable universe when it was 1,000 times smaller than it is today. These variations reveal the underlying gravitational effects of dark mass-energy fluctuations left over from an even earlier time: a filtered glimpse of the primordial universe.

New satellite experiments measuring the polarization of this microwave radiation could reveal more details of the primordial universe. The systematic mapping of the gravitational distortions of images of the distant universe by intervening matter (gravitational lensing) enables charting the development of structure in the universe and probing both dark matter and dark energy. Large samples of distant supernovae and of galaxies and clusters will be used to study the expansion history of the universe and thereby get at the nature of the dark energy. Will the current models survive these tests? The answer to this question is not certain, but it is certain that discoveries arising from this new exploration will illuminate the origins of our world.

collapsed long ago in a big crunch or have expanded so rapidly that it would be nearly devoid of matter today. The big bang model also does not explain the origin of the lumpiness in the distribution of the matter that grew to form stars and galaxies.

One of the great successes of cosmology over the past two decades has been the development and initial testing of the "inflationary paradigm," which extends the big bang model and explains the large size and uniformity of the universe as well as the origin of the lumpiness. In the inflationary scenario, vacuum energy, not ordinary matter, dominated the energy density of the universe during the first moments of the big bang. This vacuum energy drove a rapid expansion of the universe, which homogenized it by stretching a microscopic patch to a size much larger than our visible universe. The effect of the vacuum energy of inflation is similar in many respects to that of the dark energy that physicists think may be driving the recently observed acceleration of the expansion of the universe, although the underlying physical mechanism may be different (see Chapter 5). This expansion made the geometry of the universe nearly flat; this is one of the basic predictions of inflation.

Astronomical observations, however, suggest that the density of ordinary matter is not sufficient to satisfy the equations of Einstein gravity for a flat universe, in apparent contradiction with the inflationary prediction. The total amount of matter inferred from astronomical observations falls short of that needed for a flat universe by a factor of about 3. However, recent observations of distant supernovae seem to indicate that the additional matter/energy to make the universe flat exists as a new state of mass-energy, dubbed dark energy. Moreover, measurements of the tiny temperature variations in the CMB across the sky also point to a flat universe (see Chapter 5).

The nature of this dark energy and of dark matter remains a mystery and is the focus of Chapter 5. However, the absence of a precise identification of dark matter particles and the lack of a fundamental understanding of the nature of dark energy do not prevent calculations within the inflationary paradigm that connect the physics of the early universe to observations of the CMB and of galaxies and clusters today. These calculations are key to testing inflation.

HOW DID THE UNIVERSE GET ITS LUMPS?

The 30 microkelvin variations in the temperature of the CMB from point to point on the sky indicate that the initial big bang explosion was not perfectly uniform. These variations in the CMB temperature, discovered by the COBE satellite and studied in more than 20 other experiments since (see Figure 4.1), indicate that the initial distribution of matter in the universe was lumpy, varying by about 0.001 percent from place to place. Such a small deviation from perfect smoothness may seem unimportant, but it is absolutely crucial: The attractive effect of gravity acting over the past 13 billion years has turned this tiny lumpiness into the structure that exists today. (In fact, it continues to exert an inexorable pull on matter, as the collision in Figure 4.2 suggests.) Moreover, the level of lumpiness revealed by COBE and other experiments is just what is needed to account for the structure observed today. This is one of the great successes of the hot big bang cosmology.

The existence of the lumpiness that was revealed by COBE raises a very fundamental question: How did the universe get its lumps?

The Heisenberg uncertainty principle prohibits precise knowledge of the energy density of the universe at the atomic scale, which leads to a fundamental source of lumpiness. Unfortunately, the tremendous mismatch between the subatomic length scales on which quantum fluctuations are important and the astrophysical scales associated with the structure in the universe renders this uncertainty principle possibility completely irrelevant in the standard big bang model.

Inflation changes all that. The tremendous spurt of growth that is the hallmark of inflation bridges the gap, stretching subatomic scales to astrophysical size. Further, inflationary models make detailed predictions for the statistical properties of the lumpiness that arises from quantum fuzziness. There are three key tests of the inflationary prediction that the largest structures in the universe owe their origin to the quantum fuzziness of the subatomic world.

The first test involves a comparison of the structure that exists in the universe today with that expected from the inflationary picture. If, as is currently believed, the dark matter consists of particles that are moving slowly (so-called cold dark matter), then calculations and computer simulations show that the gravitational clumping of this dark matter around the fluctuations left from inflation leads directly to the formation of galaxies and clusters of galaxies. The large-scale distribution of the galaxies and clusters that emerge from these calculations agrees well with the observed distribution. More precise tests will come when larger, more precise surveys of the universe—such as the Sloan Digital Sky Survey and the Two-Degree Field mapping project—are complete (see Figure 4.3).

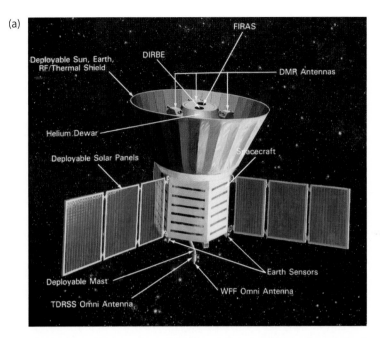

FIGURE 4.1 (a) NASA's COsmic Background Explorer (COBE) satellite as depicted orbiting Earth. COBE was launched in 1989 and made precision measurements of the CMB radiation and discovered the 30 microkelvin variation in its intensity across the sky; image courtesy of NASA. (b) Measurements made by the Balloon Observation of Millimetric Extragalactic Radiation and Geophysics (BOOMERanG) balloon experiment launched in 1998 helped to establish that the universe is flat; image courtesy of the BOOMERanG Collaboration. (c) The Degree Angular Scale Interferometer (DASI) telescope in Antartica. Measurements by DASI showed that the density of ordinary matter is small (about 4 percent) and revealed the first evidence of CMB polarization; image courtesy of the DASI Collaboration.

FIGURE 4.2 Hubble Space Telescope view of the distant universe showing a spiral galaxy as it is torn apart by collision with a smaller, more compact galaxy visible in blue in the upper left. Residing 420 million light-years away in the constellation Draco, strong gravitational forces from the interaction created a long tail of debris consisting of stars and gas that stretch out more than 280,000 light-years. Image courtesy of NASA, H. Ford, G. Illingworth, M. Clampin, G. Hartig, ACS Science Team, and ESA.

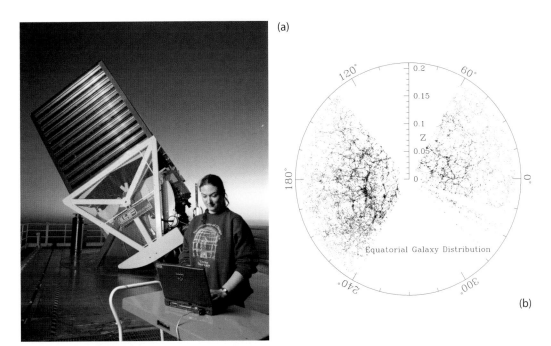

FIGURE 4.3   The Sloan Digital Sky Survey (SDSS) project uses a telescope in New Mexico to make a de-tailed map of the night sky. (a) Constance Rockosi, a graduate student at the University of Chicago and a member of the multi-institutional team that built the digital scanning camera for the Sloan Digital Sky Survey, checks the status of the instrument during its first on-the-sky trial runs in May 1998. (b) Based on the data collected through April 2002, the team released this map of one sector of the visible universe. The filaments, walls, and voids within the structure defined by the positions of about 65,000 galaxies define the "large-scale structure" of the universe. Images courtesy of Fermilab Visual Media Services.

The second test can directly probe the primeval lumpiness itself, before gravity has enhanced it. The lumpiness produced by inflation also manifests itself in local variations in the temperature of the CMB, which are directly related to the lumpiness in the distribution of matter. The inflationary model makes detailed predictions for the statistical properties of the fluctuations on the cosmic background microwave sky. The predictions are consistent with the CMB fluctuations measured by the COBE satellite on large angular scales (see Figure 4.4) and by a host of other CMB experiments on smaller angular scales. More definitive measurements will be made by a combina-tion of Earth-based, balloon-borne, and spaceborne instruments over the first decade of the new century.

In particular, NASA's Microwave Anisotropy Probe (MAP), launched in June 2001, is mapping the entire microwave sky using measurements from

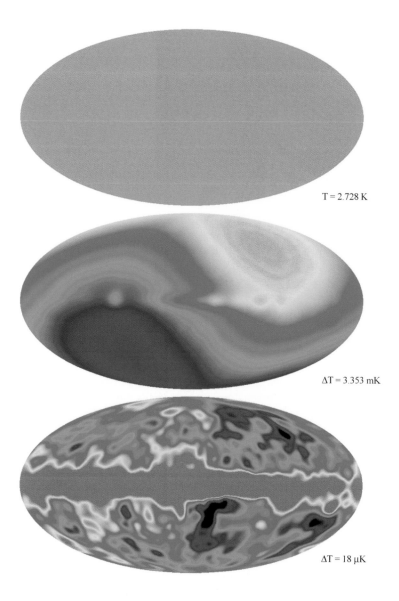

FIGURE 4.4   False color maps of the temperature of the CMB measured by the Differential Microwave Radiometer (DMR) on COBE from the 4-year dataset. The top image shows the remarkable uniformity of the CMB, which testifies to the large-scale homogeneity of the universe. The middle image shows the dipole anisotropy due to the motion of the solar system at 370 km/sec. The bottom image shows the 30-microkelvin fluctuations discovered by COBE that rose from the small (0.001 percent) variations in primeval matter density (the bright band across the middle is the microwave emission from our own galaxy). Image courtesy of NASA.

over a million independent patches and will provide precision tests of the temperature fluctuation predictions of the inflationary model (see MAP in Figure 4.5). Later in the decade, the European Space Agency's Planck Surveyor will make even higher-resolution maps of the whole sky. If the data are consistent with inflation, then the statistical properties of the CMB fluctuations can be used to learn much about the universe. Included in this list are basic cosmological parameters, such as the size of the universe and the rate at which it is expanding, the average density of ordinary matter, the average density of dark matter particles, and the amount of dark energy, as well as basic parameters of inflation.

The third test involves a detailed comparison of the two maps of the universe just discussed with other observations, including the distribution of dark matter revealed by gravitational lensing surveys (see Chapter 5). These

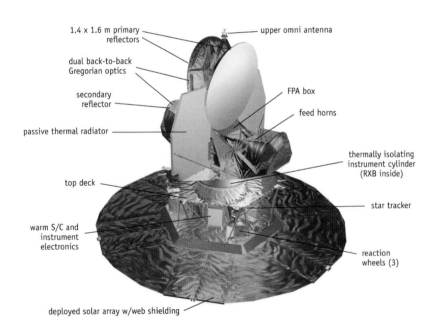

FIGURE 4.5 The MAP satellite as designed and launched in June 2001. To address its key scientific questions, MAP measures small variations in the temperature of the cosmic microwave background radiation with 30 times the angular resolution of the decade-earlier COBE satellite. The first significant results are expected in early 2003. Image courtesy of NASA.

comparisons not only will test inflation but also will determine cosmological parameters more precisely and test the underlying cosmological framework.

Although measurements of microwave background temperature fluctuations alone have the ability to discount the inflationary model or to establish it as a basic tenet of cosmology, they will not allow researchers to distinguish among different versions of inflation. Most of the current versions of inflation are simple models that show that the inflationary physics is plausible, but they are not yet closely linked to theories of the elementary particles physics such as string theory, the current best hope for unifying gravity with the other fundamental forces.

THE ORIGIN OF MATTER: WHY ARE WE HERE?

Physicists speculate that during the first microsecond of the big bang, the universe underwent a series of phase transitions. Prior to the "electroweak" phase transition, electromagnetic and weak forces were unified in a single electroweak force. Afterward, this unification or symmetry was broken and the two forces had rather different properties. Similarly, prior to the "grand unification" phase, the electroweak force and the strong force were unified as a single force. Physicists speculate that the universe began in a state of symmetry among all the forces and with equal amounts of matter and antimatter (if inflation took place, the balance between matter and antimatter is automatic). Then, around the time of either the electroweak phase transition or the grand unification phase transition, a sequence of events called baryogenesis is believed to have occurred that was responsible for the origin of the slight imbalance between matter and antimatter. As a result of baryogenesis, in the early universe there were 299,999,999 antiprotons for every 300,000,000 protons. During the first minutes of the big bang, the antiprotons annihilated and destroyed all but the one excess proton. Without baryogenesis, all of the protons in the universe would have been annihilated through collisions with an equal number of antiprotons, leaving no ordinary matter left to form stars and planets. The details of baryogenesis are not yet understood in any detail. When they are, baryogenesis will be as fundamental a part of our understanding of the evolution of the universe as big bang nucleosynthesis, which explains the origin of the lightest nuclei, is today.

Three decades ago, the Soviet physicist and dissident Andrei Sakharov identified the key ingredients for generating the matter-antimatter imbalance. These include reactions that do not create or destroy baryons and antibaryons in pairs and reactions that are not the same for matter and antimatter. Experiments can probe these reactions. If baryons can be created and destroyed, then protons could be unstable. Grand unified theories predict that the proton is unstable but very long-lived. Terrestrial experiments have searched for a variety of modes into which the proton could decay and have set remarkable limits on the order of 10^{32} years for its lifetime. Further progress will require even larger detectors. Ongoing studies are attempting to determine the feasibility of this next effort (see Chapter 3). Reactions that occur at different rates for matter and antimatter (so-called CP violation; see Chapter 2) are under intense study at particle accelerators. It is also possible the needed baryon asymmetry arose from an inequality between neutrinos and antineutrinos and involves CP violation in the neutrino sector.

GRAVITATIONAL WAVES: WHISPERS FROM THE EARLY UNIVERSE

Gravitational waves produced in the first moments of the universe can propagate directly to detectors without being altered by the intervening matter. Observations of primordial gravitational waves, although very challenging, are potentially the most powerful probe of the early universe. What are the possible sources of cosmic gravitational waves?

Today, all quarks are bound together into either protons or neutrons. However, during the first 10 microseconds of the big bang, the temperature of the universe was so high that unbound quarks moved freely in a state of matter called quark-gluon plasma. The transition from free quarks to bound quarks as the universe cooled is called the quantum chromodynamics phase transition.

Other phase transitions probably occurred. At least two symmetry-breaking phase transitions are expected: the electroweak and grand unification symmetry-breaking phase transitions, described above.

If they were violent enough, any of these phase transitions could have produced a cosmic background of gravitational waves—the gravity-wave static that new instruments can detect. The characteristic wavelength of these emitted gravitational waves corresponds to the size of the visible universe when this phase transition occurred. Compactification of putative extra dimensions may have produced a spectrum of gravitational waves. Various versions of string cosmology also predict a background of gravitational waves. Since current understanding of the physics of strings is incomplete, these sources of gravitational waves are even more speculative than the sources associated with phase transitions. Gravitational-wave observations are a unique window onto to the earliest moments of the universe and to physics that is not accessible in an Earth-based laboratory.

Currently, the best-motivated source of primordial gravitational waves is associated with inflation. These gravitational waves arise directly as quantum fluctuations in space-time itself. Their amplitude is directly related to the energy scale of inflation. In some inflationary models, there is a predicted relationship between the amplitude and wavelength of the gravitational waves and the amplitude and wavelength of the density fluctuations that grew to form galaxies. These density fluctuations are the dominant source of CMB fluctuations, but gravitational waves can also make a contribution, depending on the specific relationship between amplitude and wavelength. The upcoming MAP and Planck Surveyor satellites will be able to detect the gravitational wave contribution if it is present to a sufficient degree.

An even more promising avenue is to study the polarization of the CMB radiation. The electrons and protons in the early universe can respond to gravitational waves. They can also scatter and polarize light, producing both variations in the microwave temperature and a particular pattern in the polarization of the microwave radiation on large angular scales that carries the imprint of the gravitational wave perturbations. Since both density fluctuations and gravitational waves produce variations in the microwave background temperature, it is difficult to detect gravitational waves with temperature measurements alone. However, gravitational waves produce a unique pattern of polarization fluctuations that can be easily distinguished from that produced by density fluctuations.

So far, no gravitational wave signature in the polarization of the CMB has been detected. (Recent results from the DASI experiment have proven the ability to measure the polarization of the CMB, as seen in Figure 4.6). A variety of techniques and technologies are being tried in small-scale ground-based and balloon experiments. NASA's MAP satellite has the sensitivity to detect the polarization predicted to arise from the density fluctuations that seeded structure. Whether or not MAP is able to make this detection depends upon the unknown competing polarization signal associated with point sources and other galactic and extragalactic foregrounds. Unlike the experiments studying temperature fluctuations, the key sources of systematic errors have not been identified and controlled for. However, over the next few years, the combination of MAP and several ground-based and balloon-based experiments will measure the galactic polarization foregrounds over a wide range of frequencies and should enable detection of the polarization signal produced by density fluctuations. If the gravitational-wave signal is particularly strong, then these experiments may be able to detect it. However, detection of the gravitational-wave signal will likely

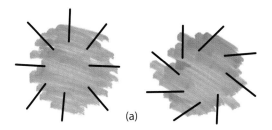

(a)

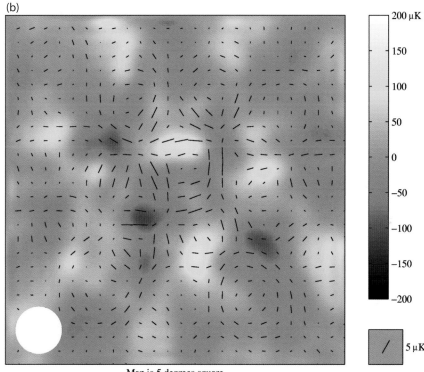

(b)

200 μK

150

100

50

0

−50

−100

−150

−200

5 μK

Map is 5 degrees square

FIGURE 4.6 (a) A cartoon sketch showing polarization measurements of the CMB. The small temperature variations in the CMB are shown in false color, with yellow hot and red cold. The polarization of each spot is shown by a black line segment. The length of the line segment shows the strength of the polarization, and the orientation shows the direction in which the radiation is polarized. E-mode polarization (left) is characterized by a radial pattern and B-mode (right) polarization is indicated by a circulation pattern. (b) An image of the intensity and polarization of the CMB radiation made from DASI at the South Pole. The white spot in the corner shows the approximate angular resolution of DASI's polarimeter. This measurement, the first of its kind, is the type necessary to detect gravity waves through CMB polarization maps. Image courtesy of the DASI Collaboration.

require a new satellite beyond MAP and the Planck Surveyor. Measurements of polarization fluctuations with high sensitivity on a large angular scale will require the benign environment of space. Once the upcoming generation of experiments improves understanding of the foregrounds and of the potential sources of systematic error, it should be possible to begin designing the next-generation polarization satellite.

A second method is the direct search for gravitational-wave static not associated with any particular astrophysical event (such as a catastrophic collision of two black holes) but rather constituting a random background radiation. The first major step is being taken with the ground-based Laser Interferometer Gravitational-wave Observatory (LIGO) and with parallel projects in Europe and Japan, which should be collecting data in 2 years and for which extensive upgrades are planned over the coming decade. However, these detectors will not operate at long wavelengths. A spaceborne laser interferometric detector could be sensitive to very-long-wavelength gravitational waves. Although gravity-wave detectors have been designed to detect point sources of gravitational radiation, they might be able to observe the diffuse radiation from the inflationary era of the early universe predicted by some models, and they would certainly be sensitive to waves from phase transitions or other exotic epochs that have been hypothesized. As the history of the CMB shows, the detection of a diffuse-noise background is far more difficult than detection of point sources. Some researchers have begun to envision multiple space-based detectors operating simultaneously and optimized to detect the cosmic background of gravitational waves.

EVEN BEFORE INFLATION: THE INITIAL CONDITIONS

While the big bang model and the inflationary universe paradigm answer many of the questions about the physical conditions in the early universe, they do not answer the most fundamental cosmology question: How did the universe begin? One approach to understanding the initial conditions for the universe is quantum cosmology, an attempt to apply the laws of quantum mechanics to the universe itself. Familiar laws of physics, such as Newton's laws or Einstein's theory of relativity, describe how physical systems evolve given an externally specified set of initial conditions. In cosmology, there is no "rest of the universe" from which to set those conditions, so a complete cosmological theory of initial conditions is needed in addition to dynamical physical laws. Whether quantum cosmology will lead to such an understanding of initial conditions, and, if so, whether it will make predictions that can be tested are deeply interesting but very open questions.

NEW OPPORTUNITIES

The inflationary paradigm is a bold attempt to extend the big bang model backward to the first moments of the universe. It uses some of the most fundamental ideas in particle physics (e.g., symmetry breaking and vacuum energy) to answer many of the basic questions of cosmology. Because of these deep connections, advances in elementary particle physics and cosmology will come hand in hand.

A number of opportunities are now ripe for answering some of the central questions of the inflationary picture. Is the inflationary picture correct? If so, what is the physics of inflation? Were there phase transitions in the early universe associated with changes in the symmetries of the underlying physics? Are the gravitational whispers detectable? It may well be possible to answer he boldest question we can ask—How did the universe begin?

How Did the Universe Begin?

In the coming years, observations will provide more stringent tests of the inflationary model. Experiments that map the fluctuations of the microwave background on finer angular scales, together with weak gravitational lensing surveys, can measure the size and the rate of expansion of the universe, the density of ordinary and dark matter, and the basic parameters of inflation. Measurements of microwave background polarization fluctuations will be sensitive to primordial gravitational waves, possibly yielding clues to the physics that underlies inflation.

What Are the New States of Matter at Exceedingly High Density and Temperature?

The direct detection of long-wavelength gravitational waves will enable scientists to "listen to" phase transitions in the early universe. This ability will require new experiments, probably space-based, designed to look for the background of gravitational waves produced in the early universe. If successful, these observations could reveal exotic states of matter in the hot, early universe, including quark-gluon plasma.

5

What Is the Nature of Dark Matter and Dark Energy?

AN EMERGING COSMIC RECIPE

What is the universe made of? The answer to this very simple question is not so simple. Baryons, the familiar neutrons and protons of which we, Earth, and the stars are made of, do not account for most of the mass in the universe. Instead, we appear to live in a universe composed primarily of new, unfamiliar, and unidentified forms of matter and energy. Three main pieces of evidence support this conclusion.

Big bang nucleosynthesis, the very successful theory of the nuclear origin of the lightest elements in the periodic table, together with recent measurements of the amount of deuterium (heavy hydrogen) in the universe, indicates that only about 4 percent of the mass and energy in the universe is in the form of ordinary matter (baryons), with the rest in an unknown form.

Since the pioneering work of Fritz Zwicky in the 1930s, astronomers have suspected that a dark component of matter—one that neither emits nor absorbs light—accounts for most of the mass of the universe. Over the last decade, the astronomy community reached a consensus that dark matter is ubiquitous in galaxies and accounts for most of the mass of clusters of galaxies and superclusters (larger systems composed of several clusters). *Most of the mass of our universe is in dark matter.* Further, because of the sheer quantity of dark matter, more than can be accounted for in the form of ordinary matter, it must be made of something exotic—with elementary particles produced in the early hot universe being the leading candidate. The leading candidate particles are axions and neutralinos (see Chapter 3).

Over the last few years, astronomers have made an even more remarkable and more puzzling discovery about the composition of the universe. Using high-redshift type Ia supernovae to probe the expansion history of the universe, they have found evidence that the expansion is speeding up, and not slowing down as expected. This result implies the existence of large amounts of "dark energy" whose gravitational force is repulsive (see Box 5.1).

Perhaps the biggest puzzle of all is the odd mix that makes up our universe—ordinary matter, exotic dark matter, and dark energy, all in significant amounts. This odd arrangement may imply, as the Ptolemaic epicycles did, that we are lacking a deep enough understanding of the laws of physics underlying our universe. It is even possible that what we call dark matter and dark energy are the signatures of some unknown aspect of gravity or space-time itself.

The Universe Is Flat

According to Einstein's theory of general relativity, the total density of matter and energy (mass or energy per unit volume) in the universe determines the spatial curvature of the universe (see Box 5.2). For one density— the so-called critical density—the universe is uncurved ("flat") and the geometry is just that of Euclid. A supercritical (closed) universe curves back on itself (like the surface of a balloon, only in all three dimensions rather than two), and a subcritical (open) universe is curved away from itself, like a saddle. The contributions to the composition of the universe mentioned above sum to a value close to the critical density, indicating a flat universe.

The cosmic microwave background (CMB) can also be used to determine the shape of the universe and thereby provide an independent accounting of the total amount of matter and energy. The angular size of the hot and cold spots in the microwave background is directly related to the shape of the universe—in a closed universe the hot and cold spots appear larger than in a flat or open universe, because the overall curvature of space acts as a cosmic lens, magnifying or demagnifying the spots (see Figure 5.1). Researchers have recently made spectacular progress with the measurement of the angular scale of the hot and cold spots on the CMB. The BOOMERanG, MAXIMA, and DASI experiments have confirmed indications from earlier experiments that the universe is indeed flat, which implies a density deviating from the critical density by at most 6 percent.

These CMB experiments not only have determined the shape of the universe but also have provided an important cross-check on the accounting of the composition of the universe. Future CMB experiments, including the MAP and the Planck satellite missions, should reveal important clues about the nature of the dark matter and dark energy. However, more experiments will ultimately be needed to clarify the nature of both.

BOX 5.1   EINSTEIN'S GRAVITY CAN BE REPULSIVE

The most familiar feature of gravity is that it pulls, not pushes. According to Newton's theory the gravitational force exerted by an object is always attractive and proportional to its mass. Not so, according to Einstein—in unusual circumstances gravity can be repulsive. Einstein's theory, which extends our understanding of gravity into situations when gravity is very strong or particles move very fast, has other more familiar, amazing features, including black holes.

While the central idea of Einstein's theory is the description of gravity as a property of curved space rather than a force, one can still discuss Einstein's gravity in terms of forces. Because mass and energy are related through Einstein's most famous equation, $E = mc^2$, it is not surprising that energy replaces mass in Einstein's version of a gravitational force. What is new is that pressure also generates gravity. (Recall that pressure can be thought of as momentum flowing in a particular direction.) When thinking of gravity as force in general relativity, it is the energy and the pressure ($E + 3P$) that determine the strength of the gravitational force exerted by an object.

The pressure of an ordinary gas is outward and positive. According to Einstein's equations then, the gravitational pull of a ball of hot gas (e.g., our Sun) is greater than that of an equivalent mass of cold particles that have no pressure. For most situations the difference is too small to be of any importance. However, it is precisely this feature of Einstein's theory that leads to the prediction of black holes, objects that cannot support themselves against the force of gravity and collapse to a singularity. For example, in any stationary object like the Sun or Earth the force of gravity must be balanced by an outward pressure if the object is to retain its shape and size. (In our Sun, the pressure arises from the hot gas of which it is made.) The extra gravitational force due to the pressure term is small. In more massive objects gravity is stronger and the corresponding resisting pressure must be stronger. But as the pressure increases, the correction to the pull of gravity also increases. For very massive objects, the extra gravitational forces due to the pressure itself can exceed the outward push of the pressure itself (remember the factor of 3 in front of pressure in the gravitational force equation) and is counterproductive. For very massive objects, in the end the pressure that initially supports the object against gravity only hastens the collapse to a black hole.

Although there are good reasons to believe that energy cannot be negative, negative pressure is a feature of anything that is elastic (e.g., a rubber band or sheet of rubber). For a rubber sheet or a rubber band, the small decrease in the gravitational attraction is too small to measure. However, there are situations in which the pressure can be comparable in magnitude to the energy, but negative, so that gravity becomes repulsive. The most extreme case is the energy of the quantum vacuum, where the pressure is the exact opposite of the energy, with the result that the gravitational pull is not only twice what Newton would predict but also repulsive! In Einstein's theory of gravity, repulsive gravity is possible, but in Newton's theory it is not.

In constructing his original static model of our universe, Einstein tuned one feature of his theory: He balanced the attractive force of matter in the universe against the repulsive force of his cosmological constant, which is mathematically equivalent to vacuum energy (described above). If the expansion of the universe is indeed speeding up and not slowing down, as current observations indicate, one need not go beyond Einstein's theory for an explanation. We are simply seeing a new feature of gravity.

Not Much Ordinary Matter

There is now much evidence that the kind of matter we are made of accounts for only a small amount (around 4 percent) of the total mass and energy budget of the universe. Three independent methods point to this conclusion (see Figure 5.2).

During the first 3 minutes after the big bang, protons and neutrons fused together to form the nuclei of the lightest elements in the periodic table, hydrogen, deuterium (heavy hydrogen), tritium, helium, and lithium. The relative abundance of these elements, particularly deuterium, is sensitive to the density of ordinary matter. The recent measurement of the primordial

---

BOX 5.2   UNDERSTANDING THE CURVATURE OF SPACE-TIME

The central idea of Einstein's theory of relativity is the curvature of space-time. While it is difficult (if not impossible) to visualize curved three-dimensional space, the tools of modern mathematics can describe it readily. However, it is possible to visualize a lower dimensional curved space. Imagine a universe with only two spatial dimensions, rather than the three of our space time. The two-dimensional analogue of our universe can take on three different shapes: flat, like a sheet of ordinary paper; positively curved (closed), like the surface of a ball; or negatively curved (open), like a saddle (or a potato chip), as shown in Figure 5.2.1.

Viewed from the luxury of our three space dimensions, these two-dimensional universes are seen to be very different. However, there are also simple mathematical measurements that the hypothetical two-dimensional inhabitants of these universes could make to discover the shape of their universe. The simplest involves one of the most basic truths of Euclidean geometry: In flat (Euclidean) space, the angles of a triangle sum to 180 degrees. This is not true for the open or closed spaces: for the

closed universe (surface of a ball), the angles in a triangle always sum to greater than 180 degrees, and for the open universe (saddle) the sum is always less than 180 degrees. Without escaping to three dimensions, the two-dimensional inhabitants of these curved universes can determine the shape of their universe.

We can do the same. The trick in all of this is using really big triangles. In a tiny triangle laid out on the surface of a ball, the amount by which the angles exceed 180 degrees is too small to measure. In our universe, the largest triangle we can lay out extends to the surface of last scattering for the CMB. Measuring the size of hot and cold spots on the microwave sky uses the triangle method to determine the shape of our universe. The physical size of these spots depends on simple physics and not on the shape of the universe. However, the angular size of the spots does depend on the shape, through the triangle effect just discussed. By measuring the size of these spots, the BOOMERanG, MAXIMA, and DASI experiments were in essence determining the sum of the angles in the largest triangle we can lay out.

(continued on next page)

BOX 5.2   *(continued)*

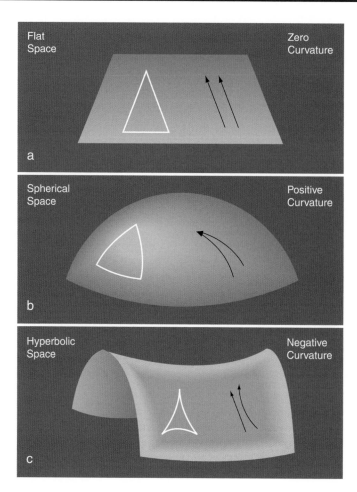

FIGURE 5.2.1   Three-dimensional curved space is not possible to visualize, but curvature in two dimensions can be illustrated. A positively curved universe is like the surface of a sphere; a negatively curved universe, like a saddle. A universe with zero curvature is like a plane. The geometry of curved space, two- or three-dimensional, is different: parallel lines may intersect (positively curved space) or may diverge (negatively curved space) and the sum of angles in a triangle may be more than 180 degrees (positively curved space) or less than 180 degrees (negatively curved space). The CMB determination of the curvature of space relied upon these facts.

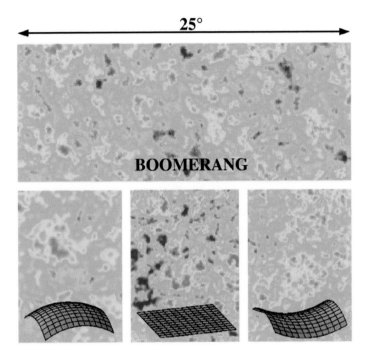

FIGURE 5.1   The pattern of hot and cold spots on the cosmic microwave background (CMB) sky expected in a high-density, closed universe; in a critical-density, flat universe; and in a low-density, open universe (bottom, from left to right) and the real map of the CMB sky made by the BOOMERanG experiment (top). The tiny temperature variations map the distribution of matter 400,000 years after the big bang; their angular size is determined by the shape of the universe. The BOOMERanG results indicate that we live in a spatially flat universe. Image courtesy of the BOOMERanG Collaboration.

deuterium abundance in primeval gas clouds along the line of sight to distant quasars has provided a precision measurement of the average baryon density, about 4 percent of the critical density.

Secondly, the statistical properties of the fluctuations in the cosmic microwave background are sensitive to the baryon density. For example, when one takes pairs of points on the sky, calculates the difference in the microwave temperature between those points, and then looks at many pairs and many angles between the pairs, one finds that for some angles the temperature differences are larger than for others. When plotted as a function of angle, the curve shows peaks and valleys in the temperature differences. The higher the baryon density, the larger the ratio between the

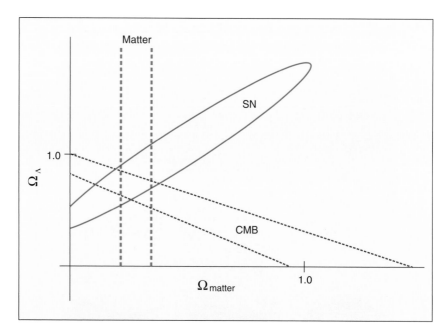

FIGURE 5.2   Concordance of the three independent measurements of the mass/
energy density of the universe, as indicated by their intersection. The two axes are the
dark energy (vertical) and matter (horizontal). The ellipse denotes the supernova measurements, which indicate that the expansion of the universe is speeding up. The vertical lines correspond to measurements of the dark matter density and the sloping triangle represents the CMB measurements that indicate a flat, critical universe (here,
matter plus dark energy sum to one).

amplitude of the first and second peaks in this plot. The results from
BOOMERanG, MAXIMA and DASI (see Figure 5.3) give a value of the
baryon density consistent with the density determined from big bang nucleosynthesis, but with a slightly larger uncertainty.

The third method, like the first, involves the study of primeval gas in the
universe by its absorption of light from distant quasars. In this case, the total
amount of light absorbed can be used to estimate the total amount of
ordinary matter that existed in the universe only a few billion years after the
big bang. The results of these studies, which are not as precise, are also
consistent with a baryon density of only about 4 percent of the critical
density.

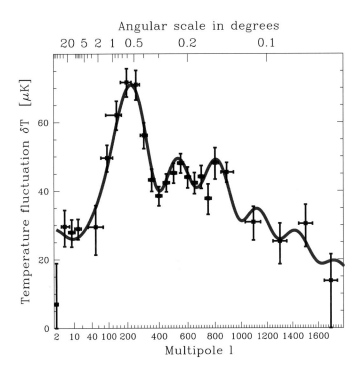

FIGURE 5.3   Power spectrum of cosmic microwave background (CMB) fluctuations measured by the BOOMERanG, MAXIMA, and DASI experiments. The height of the curve is a measure of temperature differences, while the horizontal axis is a measure of the angular separation, with larger values of *l* corresponding to smaller angles. The position of the first peak indicates that we live in a flat universe; the ratio of the amplitudes of the first and second peaks indicates a baryon density of around 4 percent, consistent with the big bang nucleosynthesis determination. The solid curve is the theoretical prediction for a flat universe whose composition is 4 percent ordinary matter, 29 percent cold dark matter, and 67 percent dark energy. Image courtesy of M. Tegmark and M. Zaldarriaga, 2002.

These three methods of baryon accounting measure the amount of ordinary matter when the universe was a few minutes old, about a half million years old, and a few billion years old, respectively. While these results are consistent, it would also be nice to have a similar accounting of ordinary matter today.

Such an accounting is more difficult because stars have been born and have died, baryons have been stirred up by the process of structure formation, and the universe is a more complicated place than it was long ago. Today baryons exist in bright stars, hot and cold gas, dark stars (faint stars such as white dwarfs, neutron stars, and black holes), and perhaps in other forms. A census of bright stars and cold gas shows that they account for only one third of the density inferred from big bang nucleosynthesis. The rest of the baryons are "dark" (see Figure 5.4).

Where are the dark baryons, and in what form do they exist? The most likely form is hot gas filling the regions between galaxies, the so-called hot intergalactic medium. Hot gas in the intergalactic medium is difficult to observe directly. Astronomers do have hints from observations of diffuse x-ray emission and from measurements of light absorption that there are significant quantities of gas in the hot intergalactic medium, but they are unable to characterize the quantity more precisely. Within our own galaxy, there is evidence that some of the dark baryons exist in the form of old white dwarfs.

While there is no evidence that the amount of ordinary matter today exceeds the big bang nucleosynthesis estimate, a full accounting of ordinary matter today is lacking. Such an accounting is high on the list of what astronomers would like to accomplish during the current decade.

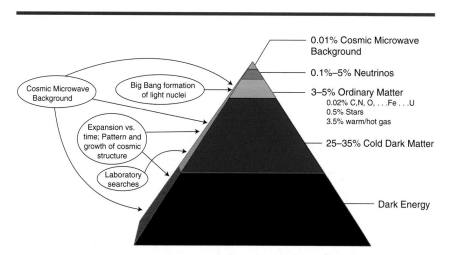

FIGURE 5.4 Pyramid diagram of the composition of the universe and the different techniques that can be used to measure the various components. For instance, evidence for dark matter comes from cosmic microwave background radiation and the pattern of cosmic structure. Laboratory searches have the potential to identify dark matter by detecting halo dark matter particles or producing it in accelerators.

EXOTIC DARK MATTER

Baryons account only for about 4 percent of the critical density, and several lines of evidence point to a matter density that is 35 percent of the critical density. The large discrepancy between these two numbers is the linchpin in the case for exotic (nonbaryonic) dark matter. While the additional matter cannot be seen with telescopes, its gravitational effects—from holding galaxies and clusters together to playing a critical role in the formation of large-scale structure—are very visible.

Evidence for the Existence of Dark Matter

The existence of dark matter is now well established on a variety of scales. In large spiral galaxies it is possible to measure the rotation velocity of gas clouds out to large distances from their centers. The behavior of rotation velocities implies that there is substantial mass well beyond the distance at which no more stars are observed and that the bulk of the matter that holds spiral galaxies together exists in a dark, extended halo (see Figure 5.5). Similar

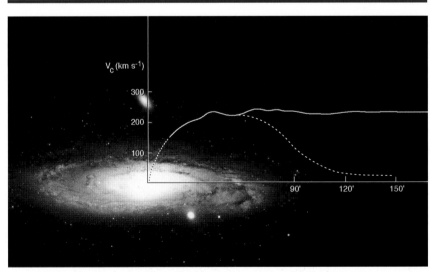

FIGURE 5.5   An image of the Andromeda galaxy with its rotation curve (velocity of gas clouds and stars orbiting the center of the galaxy vs. distance from the center). The constancy (flatness) of the rotation curve beyond the point where the light ends indicates the presence of dark matter that holds the galaxy together. The dashed line fading back to zero shows what the rotation curve would look like in the absence of dark matter. Image courtesy of M. Roberts.

dynamical evidence for dark matter is found in elliptical galaxies. Simply put, there is more mass than meets the eye in galaxies of all types.

The effect of dark matter is even more pronounced in clusters of galaxies. Cluster galaxies move at high speeds, and the mass necessary to hold them together in the cluster far exceeds that contained in all the stars that make up the galaxies. Cluster dark matter also creates a cosmic mirage: Light emitted by distant galaxies that passes by a cluster is bent by the gravitational effect of the cluster dark matter, as predicted by Einstein's theory. Near the center of the cluster, this effect can be strong enough to produce multiple images of the distant galaxies. Farther out, it distorts the shape of each and every distant galaxy (see Figure 5.6). Gravitational lensing, as this phenomenon is called, based on one of the first tests of Einstein's theory, is now used routinely to map dark matter in clusters and individual galaxies. This method shows very directly that clusters have 100 times more mass than can be accounted for in stars.

On even larger scales, the effect of dark matter can be detected through the pull it exerts on individual galaxies. By carefully measuring the velocities and distances of thousands of galaxies, it has been shown that virtually all galaxies—including our own—move with velocities over and above the velocities expected due to the expansion of the universe. These additional "peculiar velocities," which arise from the gravitational effect of dark matter, provide a means of mapping the distribution of dark matter on scales even larger than those of clusters. This technique has revealed large dark-matter accumulations, including the well-known "Great Attractor." Again, the amounts of matter revealed far exceed those that can be accounted for in stars or even in baryons.

Finally, the gravity of the luminous matter alone is not sufficient to account for the formation of the abundance of structure seen in the universe today—from galaxies to the great walls of galaxies. As discussed in Chapter 4, all objects seen today evolved from the tiny lumpiness in the matter that existed early on and was revealed by the Cosmic Background Explorer (COBE) experiment. This process was driven by the relentless, attractive force of gravity operating over the past 13 billion years. With the level of lumpiness revealed by COBE as the starting point, the structures seen today could not have been produced by the gravitational effect of luminous matter alone.

There is little doubt that dark matter exists. Deciphering its nature remains one of the great challenges of cosmology. Because there is strong evidence that it is not made of ordinary matter, discovering dark matter's nature will also have deep implications for physics.

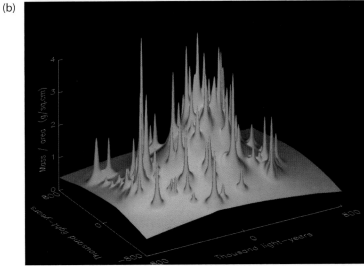

FIGURE 5.6 (a) Hubble Space Telescope image of the gravitational lensing of light from distant galaxies (distorted and multiple blue images) by a more nearby cluster (orange galaxies). (b) Derived map of the mass that must be between the distant galaxies and our observation point to cause the gravitational lensing. The height of the surface is proportional to the projected mass density. Images courtesy of NASA, W.N. Colley, E. Turner, and J.A. Tyson.

Amount of Dark Matter

How much dark matter is there? The most direct route to arriving at a quantitative estimate makes use of clusters to carry out a cosmic inventory of all forms of matter. Clusters are large objects and should offer a fair sample of matter in the universe. Thus, a measurement of the ratio of the total amount of matter to the amount of ordinary matter in a cluster can be used to determine the total amount of matter in the universe.

Most of the ordinary matter in clusters exists as hot, x-ray-emitting intracluster gas and can be inventoried from the clusters' x-ray emission or from the slight distorting effect that clusters produce on the cosmic microwave background, known as the Sunyaev-Zel'dovich effect. Both methods arrive at the same value for the amount of cluster gas. The total mass can be measured through gravitational lensing, as well as by using the galaxy motions (or temperature of the hot gas) to infer the amount of matter needed to hold the cluster baryons together; all three methods give consistent results. The ratio of the total amount of matter to the amount of ordinary matter determined for clusters (about 9 to 1) and the big bang nucleosynthesis value for the amount of ordinary matter in the universe (about 4 percent) imply that the total amount of dark matter is about 35 percent of critical density.

Measurements of the peculiar motions of galaxies and the amount of mass contained in the halos of spiral galaxies point to a total density of matter that is consistent with this estimate. Using large, supercomputer numerical simulations of the formation structure in the universe, cosmologists arrive at a similar estimate for total matter density, based upon the gravitational pull needed to form the structure seen today from the lumpiness that existed at early times.

To summarize, there is strong evidence that dark matter holds the universe together, from the smallest galaxies to the largest structures observed. Although systematic uncertainties still exist, a number of independent lines of reasoning point to a dark matter density of about 35 percent of the critical density.

Different from Ordinary Matter

Three strong lines of evidence suggest that dark matter is something other than ordinary matter. The amount of dark matter (about 35 percent of the critical density) is significantly greater than the amount of ordinary matter inferred from big bang nucleosynthesis and from the cosmic microwave background (3 percent to 5 percent of the critical density). The discrepancy is nearly a factor of 10, which is far greater than the uncertainty in either number. The amount of dark matter needed to produce the structure observed today from the lumpiness that existed early on is much greater than the known amount of ordinary matter. In addition, the pattern of structure that exists today cannot be produced even if baryons accounted for 35 percent of the critical density and there was no exotic dark matter. Putting aside the CMB and big bang nucleosynthesis measurements of the amount of ordinary matter, the implausibility of hiding 99 percent of the baryons in a form that is not detectable is daunting. For example, putting 35 percent of the critical density in white dwarfs or neutron stars would require far more star formation than the evidence supports. It is equally difficult to hide this many baryons in hot gas: Putting 35 percent of critical density in hot gas would jumble the cosmic microwave background by creating far too many hot and cold spots on the microwave sky.

Particle Debris from the Big Bang

The early universe was a powerful accelerator that produced the full complement of nature's fundamental particles. At the earliest times there was a kind of particle democracy, where all particles were present in numbers comparable to the number of cosmic background photons. Over the course of time, as the universe cooled, massive particles disappeared when they were annihilated by their antiparticles. Without special circumstances, only photons (and other massless particles) would be left today.

Ordinary matter survived because of the tiny excess of matter over antimatter (see Chapter 4). Other massive particles might have survived if their self-annihilation had not been complete. Incomplete annihilation can occur if particle interactions are weak, like those of neutrinos. Massive neutrinos survived in great numbers because their annihilations failed to destroy them quickly enough. If nature is supersymmetric, the lightest superparticle, known as the neutralino (see Chapter 3), would survive in sufficient numbers to make a major contribution to the dark matter. (There are other, more complicated ways in which a particle can survive from the early universe.)

Over the years, many particles have been discussed as candidates for dark matter. Three deserve special consideration because they solve important problems in particle physics and their efficacy as dark matter is a cosmological bonus: massive neutrinos, neutralinos, and axions.

• *Neutrinos.* Because the relic abundance of neutrinos is well determined, their contribution to the mass density of the universe hinges on the question of their masses. To account for the dark matter, one (or the combination of all three) neutrino species would need a mass of around 30 eV. As discussed in Chapter 3, there is good evidence that at least one neutrino species has mass; however, the mass indicated is much smaller than this. Further, as discussed below, the pattern of structure formation seen in the universe is not consistent with the idea that neutrinos constitute the bulk of the dark matter. In fact, the neutrino mass implied by experiment indicates that neutrinos contribute between 0.1 percent and 5 percent, about as much mass as do bright stars. Neutrinos are part of the cosmic mix. This fact gives some credence to the idea of particle dark matter.

• *Neutralinos.* The neutralino is well motivated by particle theory, it would lead to a pattern of structure formation that is consistent with observations, and it might eventually be produced at a particle accelerator with other supersymmetric particles. While estimates of its mass are uncertain, they are 50 to 500 times the mass of the proton. The neutralino is therefore a prime candidate for dark matter and for detection.

• *Axions.* The axion was postulated to cure a serious but subtle problem with the otherwise very successful theory of quantum chromodynamics. Of course, this theoretical role is no guarantee that the axion actually exists. If it does, then axions would have been produced copiously in the early universe and would have survived in sufficient numbers to account for the dark matter today, in spite of the fact that the mass predicted for the axion, between about 0.00001 and 0.001 eV/c^2, is so tiny.

These are the currently favored candidates. However, recent progress in string theory has led to a number of new ideas that could explain the dark-matter puzzle (and possibly even the dark-energy puzzle, too). Some have speculated that we and the weak, electromagnetic, and strong interactions actually live on a 4-dimensional "brane" in an 11-dimensional space, and that gravity can propagate through all 11 dimensions. If there are other branes in the 11-dimensional space, their gravitational interactions with our brane could in fact be what is called dark matter. It is also possible that the dark matter is made up of particles that are very much heavier than any of the three candidates discussed and that were produced at the end of inflation. Such ideas are at an early stage and have little predictive power. However, given their potential importance, they merit further attention.

How can progress be made in choosing between these possibilities and deciphering the nature of the dark matter? Two complementary approaches are important: characterize as much as possible the clumping properties of dark matter (a clue to its nature) and attempt to directly detect the dark matter particles in our halo and/or produce them at an accelerator.

Hot, Cold, or Something Else?

The different particle dark-matter candidates are characterized by how fast the particles are moving: dark matter whose individual particles move fast (i.e., at speeds close to that of light) is called hot, and dark matter whose individual particles move slowly (i.e., at speeds much less than that of light) is called cold. Neutrinos fall into the first category, hot dark matter, while axions and neutralinos are cold dark matter. Neutralinos move slowly because they are heavy, while axions do so because they were produced in a cold state by a quantum process akin to Bose-Einstein condensation. (Other candidates are intermediate in speed and are referred to as warm dark matter.)

The difference between hot and cold is crucial for structure formation: hot dark matter particles move fast enough to wash out lumpiness on galactic scales (particles from high-density regions spread out quickly to fill in lower-density regions). In turn, this means that galaxies must form by fragmentation of larger structures (superclusters). With cold dark matter, structure forms from the bottom up—galaxies form first, cluster together to form clusters of galaxies, and so on. In the 1980s this led to two competing theories of structure formation—the hot dark matter and cold dark matter scenarios.

The observational evidence is now very clear. Structure formed from the bottom up—galaxies came into existence before clusters of galaxies and superclusters. This fact all but rules out neutrinos (or other future hot dark matter candidates) as the dominant part of the dark matter. Moreover, the formation of structure with cold dark matter has been simulated on supercomputers, and the predictions agree well with a wide array of observations, including the masses and abundances of galaxies, clustering of galaxies and clusters of galaxies, the distribution of gas clouds at high redshift, and fluctuations in the cosmic microwave background radiation. This concordance, together with the failure of hot dark matter to account for the evidence, provides convincing indications that the dark matter particles are cold.

That being said, there are hints of problems with the cold dark matter model. Computer simulations of the evolution of cold dark matter predict more substructure within galactic halos than is seen and a higher concentration of dark matter at the centers of galaxies and clusters than is measured.

It could be that there are physical mechanisms for smoothing the dark matter distribution that are not included in the simulations or some problem in interpreting the observations. However, no such solution has yet been found. These results have given rise to speculation that the observations are revealing some new property of the dark matter.

Identifying the Dark Matter Particle

Based on clues from astrophysics, cosmology, and particle physics, progress is now being made in the search for the dark matter particles in the laboratory. After a decade of effort, attempts to look for the three main candidates are now reaching the level of sensitivity needed to test their candidacies directly.

Neutrinos

In spite of the fact that neutrinos alone cannot form the large-scale structure observed in the universe, measurements of their masses are needed to clarify the role they have in cosmology. The measuring techniques include the study of beta-decay spectra, the study of neutrinoless double-beta decay, and searches for oscillations between the different neutrino species. Neutrino oscillation studies using neutrinos produced by cosmic rays in Earth's atmosphere and by the Sun have already produced strong evidence for nonzero neutrino mass and indicate a minimum cosmic density of neutrinos comparable to the mass density of stars. At this minimum mass density, neutrinos might have a small, but detectable, influence on the formation of large-scale structure, which could permit a cosmological determination of their masses.

Neutralinos

Experimentalists are pursuing two general approaches: (1) direct detection of elastic scattering of the neutralinos that presumably exist in the halo of our galaxy in very sensitive laboratory detectors and (2) detection of the annihilation products of neutralinos that accumulate within the Sun, Earth, or the halo of our galaxy. The direct-detection field is very active, especially in Europe, with experiments based on germanium of unprecedented radioactive purity, the operation of very large sodium iodide scintillators, and the development of totally new cryogenic sensors. The DAMA collaboration at the Gran Sasso laboratory in Italy says it has detected a signature of neutralinos via a yearly modulation of the signal of ±2 percent in 100 kg of sodium iodide that would be caused by Earth's annual movement through the local cloud of neutralinos. However, the U.S.-based Cryogenic Dark Matter Search (CDMS) experiment and other experiments at European laboratories appear to contradict this result. Even if the DAMA result is not confirmed, this is an exciting time for dark matter searches, because the current generation of experiments is now achieving the sensitivity levels needed to detect neutralinos. A number of second-generation experiments (CDMS II in the United States, and CRESST II and Genius in Europe) will be even more sensitive and will explore a significant amount of the theoretically favored parameter space. Neutralinos in the galactic center and trapped in the Sun or Earth can annihilate and produce high-energy neutrinos. Neutralino annihilations in our galactic center would produce gamma rays, antiprotons, and positrons; GLAST will have significant sensitivity to the gamma-ray signature of halo neutralinos. The current generation of high-energy neutrino detectors is about as sensitive to neutralinos as are the direct-detection experiments. Finally, it is possible that the neutralino will be produced and detected in an accelerator experiment (i.e., at the Fermilab Tevatron or at CERN's Large Hadron Collider).

Axions

The most promising method for detecting axions is through their interaction within the halo of our galaxy with a very strong magnetic field. In the presence of the magnetic field, axions would produce a faint microwave radiation detectable in a tunable microwave cavity. The U.S. axion experiment has reached the sensitivity needed to begin testing the axion dark matter hypothesis. The recently approved upgrade incorporates novel SQUID amplifiers that will enable it to search for axions over a mass range spanning one order of magnitude (out of the three that are still allowed by current theories). A Japanese collaboration is developing very sensitive photon detectors using atoms in highly excited states that will cover the same mass range.

DARK ENERGY

Is Expansion of the Universe Speeding Up Rather Than Slowing Down?

Type Ia supernovae, the thermonuclear explosions of white dwarf stars slightly more massive than the Sun, have remarkably uniform peak luminosities (when corrected for the rate of decline of brightness). Since they are very bright, they can be seen and studied throughout the observable universe and can be used as cosmic mileposts to study the expansion rate of the universe at earlier times. For 70 years, astronomers have been trying to measure the slowing effect of gravity on the expansion of the universe to determine the total amount of matter in the universe. In a surprising and exciting turn of events, two teams independently studying supernovae at high redshift (corresponding to great distance) (see Figure 5.7) recently found that the expansion of the universe is speeding up, not

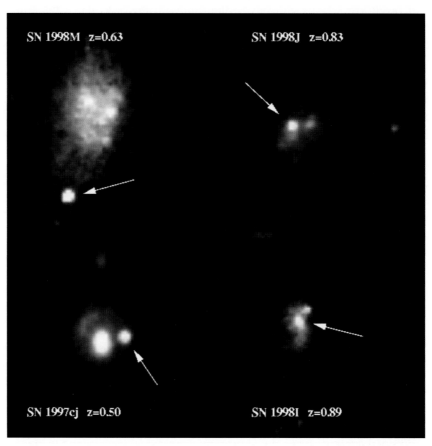

FIGURE 5.7   Images of distant Type Ia supernovae. For about a month, these thermonuclear stellar explosions produce about as much light as the rest of the stars in the galaxy combined. Image courtesy of NASA.

slowing down! The acceleration requires something new, as matter in any amount should cause the universe to decelerate. The nature of this new component, called dark energy in the spirit of Zwicky's naming of dark matter, is not understood.

Since the supernova observations yield such a surprising result, astronomers are carefully searching for sources of systematic error in their measurements or interpretations. There are a number of possible sources of error. For example, type Ia supernovae might not remain "standard" at earlier epochs. It is possible that large dust particles (so-called "gray dust") pervade intergalactic space, absorbing some of the light from distant supernovae, mimicking the effect of an accelerating universe. Thus far, no systematic error has been found that would invalidate the result.

Independent Confirmation of an Accelerating Universe

While the supernovae results themselves may be subject to unknown errors, there is an independent confirmation of the extraordinary discovery that the expansion of the universe is speeding up, not slowing down. It comes from the CMB measurements, which give a top-down accounting of matter and energy in the universe. The measurements indicate that the universe is flat; this, in turn, implies that summed together, matter and energy must equal the critical density. Since independent accounts of the amount of matter indicate that it is about 35 percent of the critical density, the CMB measurements point to another component that does not clump with matter and contributes about 65 percent of the critical density. This missing mass/energy revealed by the CMB is consistent with the dark energy component indicated by supernovae measurements.

Why Is the Expansion of the Universe Speeding Up?

According to Einstein's theory, in unusual circumstances gravity can be repulsive (see Box 5.1). What is needed is a form of energy that is elastic (negative pressure). There is a form of energy known to have this property—the energy of the quantum vacuum (originally referred to as the cosmological constant by Einstein). However, this fact does not wrap up the story of dark energy. All efforts to calculate the energy of the quantum vacuum using our current understanding of physics give a value that is at least 55 orders of magnitude (10^{55} times) too large. Perhaps advances in understanding of the quantum vacuum will ultimately solve the discrepancy, but many theorists believe that such an advance will lead to an explanation of why the vacuum energy should be precisely zero rather than the tiny but finite value needed to explain the accelerating universe.

Other explanations for the dark energy have been proposed. There is the possibility that a particle field, poetically named "Quintessence," is at work. If this were the case, we would be at the beginning of a (hopefully mild) inflationary episode. Topological defects arising from a phase transition in the early universe could get tangled and exert a negative pressure, exactly as a bunch of tangled rubber bands when one tries to separate them. Or we could be experiencing the effects of additional space-time dimensions.

The ultimate fate of the universe depends on the nature of the dark energy. If the dark energy is truly the energy of the quantum vacuum, then the fate of the universe is continued acceleration of its expansion. As a result, 150 billion years from now only a thousand or so galaxies will still be visible to even the most powerful telescope because the vast majority of galaxies in the universe will be moving away too fast to be seen. On the other hand, if the universe is only experiencing a mild and temporary spurt of inflation, then it will once again begin to slow down and the sky will remain filled with galaxies until all their stars burn out.

Finally, there is the "why now?" puzzle. We appear to live at a special time when the expansion of the universe is transitioning from deceleration to acceleration. Is this fact just a coincidence, or does it have a deeper explanation?

TWO MAJOR CHALLENGES: DECIPHERING DARK MATTER AND DARK ENERGY

Occasionally a science reaches a precipice—a juncture where all paths seem to lead to confusion. These crises often precede major conceptual breakthroughs. By any measure, cosmologists and physicists now find themselves in such a (wonderful) quandary. Their picture of the universe now requires a strange kind of dark energy with negative pressure, along with dark matter that is made of something other than the baryons that make up the stars and us.

Deciphering the nature of the dark matter and dark energy is one of the most important goals in the physics of the universe. Resolving both puzzles is key to advancing current understanding of both cosmology and particle physics. The solutions to these problems will cast light not only on the fate of the universe but also on the very nature of matter, space, and time. Through a combination of new approaches and increasingly powerful instrumentation, scientists are poised to make great progress in the coming years.

Astronomical Tools

There are several astronomical approaches to determining the properties of dark matter and dark energy. They rely on information of two different types. The expansion rate of the universe depends on its composition. By measuring the distances to objects as a function of redshift, astronomers can determine the expansion history and thereby infer the relative abundances of dark matter and dark energy, as well as probe the nature of the dark energy. The rate at which structure in the universe forms is sensitive to the properties of both the dark matter and the dark energy. On large scales, the growth rate of structure is sensitive primarily to the amount of dark energy and its properties. Once the matter collapses to form galaxies and clusters, the properties of the galaxies and clusters are sensitive to the detailed properties of the dark matter.

There are several powerful techniques for getting at the *expansion rate* of the universe. Observations of the angular size of hot and cold spots on the microwave sky can determine the distance to the surface where the radiation originated; that distance depends on the expansion history of the universe from 400,000 years ago until today. The MAP and Planck satellite missions will accurately make this measurement in the coming years.

Observations of distant supernovae can probe the detailed expansion history directly back to redshifts of around 2, corresponding to times from a few billion years after the big bang until the present. The current data have already provided the first strong evidence for the existence of dark energy. Large-field-of-view telescopes are needed to find larger and more uniform samples of supernovae. These telescopes will vastly increase the samples of supernovae (by a factor 10 or more). Large samples will enable not only greater statistical accuracy but also better control of systematic errors. For example, a large sample of supernovae can be divided into smaller subsamples to search for systematic trends and test the validity of the results.

The probability of the gravitational lensing of distant objects is sensitive to the distance to the lens and the background source; these distances depend on the expansion history of the universe. Observations of clusters containing multiple-lensed sources at several different redshifts can measure the relative distances to the lenses and sources. These observations will require detailed maps of the mass of the cluster based on gravitational lensing observations.

Like the distance to high-redshift objects in the universe, the volume associated with a given redshift is sensitive to the expansion history. Counting objects of known (or calculable) instrinsic number density can be used to infer the volume as a function of redshift, and from it the expansion history. Galaxies and clusters of fixed mass both show promise for this use.

There are several powerful techniques for probing the *growth rate* of structure in the universe. The emergence of the first stars and galaxies (a few hundred million years after the big bang) is sensitive to the nature of the dark matter. For example, hot dark matter (neutrinos) completely inhibits early galaxy formation, and the study of the formation of the large gas clouds seen by their absorption of light from distant quasars constrains the fraction of dark matter in the form of neutrinos to less than about 10 percent. Observations of "weak" gravitational lensing (i.e., the small distortions of the shapes of galaxies) can be used to measure the large-scale clustering properties of matter during the last 10 billion years. The amplitude of this clustering as a function of scale and redshift depends on the amount of dark energy and its properties. Observations of "strong" gravitational lensing measure the distribution of mass within galaxies and clusters. The density profile at the core of galaxies and clusters and the number of dwarf systems around large galaxies are sensitive tests of the properties of the dark matter. The absence of central condensation of dark matter could be indicative of new dark-matter physics—or even of an inconsistency in the paradigm of particle dark matter. Measurement of the peculiar velocities of galaxies and clusters as a function of redshift is a powerful probe of the growth of structure in the dark matter. In the next few years, supernovae can be used systematically to extend current peculiar-velocity surveys by a factor of 2. Progress can also be expected in the use of galaxy surface-brightness fluctuations to provide very accurate distance measurements (±3 percent). Using this method on huge optical telescopes with adaptive optics should allow the measurement of peculiar velocities on scales 10 times as large as is currently possible. Peculiar velocities of clusters can also be measured by using the distorting effect of the hot gas in the cluster on the microwave background (Sunyaev-Zel'dovich effect). Counts of galaxies and clusters are also sensitive to the growth rate of structure in the universe. Both the growth rate and the expansion rate affect the counts.

No one of these methods will suffice by itself. A combination of methods is needed to definitively determine the nature of dark matter and dark energy. These methods are often complementary—that is, they provide different information—but at other times, they provide important cross-checks on one another. No method is immune from the possibility of subtle or unknown systematic error, so such cross-checks are critical. The importance of complementary measurements and crosschecks is illustrated by the current data in Figure 5.2.

For the study of dark energy and dark matter, a new type of telescope may be called for. Wide field-of-view (more than 1 degree) telescopes with gigapixel charge-coupled device cameras enable the search of large regions of the sky for supernovae (type Ia supernovae occur at a rate of about 1 per second over the universe but are spread over the 40,000 square degrees of the sky) and the mapping of the distribution of dark matter on large scales.

Finally, theory and large-scale computing will play a critical role. To gain the full benefit of measurements of the development of structure in the universe, large-scale numerical simulations of the predictions of the different cold dark matter models are crucial. The need for more dynamic range and better input physics challenges existing computing resources. Likewise, a better theoretical understanding of type Ia supernovae is key to exploiting them as cosmological mileposts. Achieving this understanding will require advances in large-scale scientific computing. Currently, computing resources are often the time-limiting factor in analyzing cosmic microwave background data, and the situation will become more critical with MAP, Planck, and other experiments that give high-resolution and large-sky coverage.

Laboratory Searches

Laboratory-based experiments are a complementary approach to identifying the particle dark matter. All three dark-matter candidates—axions, neutralinos, and neutrinos—can be sought out in the laboratory. This search will involve accelerators, specialized dark-matter detectors, and large underground detectors.

Accelerators will help provide important constraints on the properties of some particle dark-matter candidates or perhaps even discover the sought-after particle (e.g., the neutralino). For example, the combination of long-baseline oscillation experiments using neutrinos from existing accelerators and future muon colliders with atmospheric and solar neutrino studies will enable unraveling the mass and mixing structure of the neutrino sector. This will make it possible to describe more precisely the role of neutrinos in structure formation to be made. The search for neutrinoless double-beta decay provides additional constraints on the properties of neutrinos. Similarly, the searches for supersymmetry at the LHC and for neutralinos in the halo of our galaxy will be complementary and will reach very similar sensitivities.

In the direct search for neutralinos, it is important to begin the preparation for third-generation detection experiments, with two possible scenarios in mind. If the second-generation experiments discover a signal, the emphasis will probably shift to obtaining directional information to link the signal to the galaxy and provide information on the halo and the distribution of dark matter within it. If the second-generation experiments fail to find a signal, the emphasis will be on techniques to reduce background signals. This second route would become compelling if supersymmetry were discovered at the Tevatron or LHC. The indirect searches for neutralinos will benefit from new instruments such as the Gamma Ray Large Area Space Telescope (GLAST), which will have the energy resolution to look for gamma rays from neutralino annihilations at the galactic center. The large-area neutrino detectors being planned should complement direct-detection experiments for high-neutralino masses. Although the primary motivations for these instruments are different (see Chapter 7), they should be designed to permit such exploration.

The challenge of searches for axions will be to extend the explored mass range to the higher end of the mass range discussed in Chapter 6, subsection "Cosmic Accelerators and High-Energy Physics." Unless broad-band methods can be devised, the current approach will have to be extended to higher frequencies using, for example, tunable "photon bandgap" cavities.

Last but not least, the tests of gravity either at small scale with Cavendish-type experiments or at large scale with equivalence-principle tests (see Chapter 3) may shed some light on the dark matter and dark energy problems. These puzzles may be a sign that scientists do not understand gravity, and some models of dark energy predict the existence of new, weaker-than-gravity forces that could be discovered with more sensitive tests of the equivalence principle.

NEW OPPORTUNITIES

As the new century begins, scientists have a first, tentative accounting of the universe: one-third matter and two-thirds dark energy, adding up to the critical density and a flat universe. This accounting raises a new set of deeper questions whose answers will have profound implications for both cosmology and particle physics and whose answering will involve both astronomers and physicists. Scientists are poised to make progress in addressing two key questions about the makeup of our universe and the very nature of space, time, and matter.

What Is Dark Matter?

Dark matter—stuff that neither emits nor absorbs light—holds the universe together. Its nature is a mystery. There is strong evidence that the bulk of it is not the ordinary matter of which we and the stars are made. The working hypothesis is that it is composed of elementary particles left over from the earliest moments of creation. The leading candidates for dark matter are new particles whose existence is predicted by theories that attempt to unify the forces and particles of nature. Showing that one (or several) of these particles compose the dark matter not only would answer a key question in cosmology but also would shed new light on the fundamental forces and particles of nature.

Clues to the nature of the dark matter will come from astronomical observations of its distribution in the universe as well as from study of the evolution of structure in the universe. There are also important opportunities to detect the dark matter particles holding our galaxy together, either directly or indirectly, by detecting the particles into which they annihilate. Accelerators may also be able to produce the dark matter particle.

What Is the Nature of Dark Energy?

Two independent lines of evidence indicate the presence of a new form of energy pervading the universe that accounts for two-thirds of the critical density and is causing the expansion of the universe to speed up rather than slow down. This is an extraordinary result, so extraordinary that the first order of business is establishing further evidence for accelerated expansion and the existence of dark energy. Assuming that it exists, this mysterious dark energy exhibits a hitherto unseen feature of gravity (it can sometimes be repulsive), and understanding its nature could lead to progress in our understanding of space, time, and matter. Explanations put forth for the dark energy range from the energy of the quantum vacuum to the influence of unseen space-time dimensions. *Science* magazine was not exaggerating when in 1998 it chose as the scientific breakthrough of the year the discovery that the expansion of the universe was accelerating.

Dark energy by its very nature is extremely diffuse, and its effect can be felt only on the largest scales, where it influences the expansion of the universe and the growth of structure within it. Getting at the nature of dark energy will necessarily involve telescopes rather than accelerators, and key opportunities exist to use supernovae, galaxies, and clusters of galaxies to probe both the expansion and the formation of structure.

In studying dark energy and dark matter a new kind of special-purpose telescope may prove useful. The mapping of dark matter with gravitational lensing and the search for distant supernovae both require the search of large swaths of sky. These searches could be achieved with a wide-field-of-view (1 degree or more) telescope and a commensurately large CCD camera (probably gigapixel or larger). The Sloan Digital Sky Survey (a project to digitize the sky and map large-scale structure, depicted in Figure 4.3) and the MACHO project (a search for dark stars in the halo of our galaxy through microlensing) have shown the value of such special-purpose telescopes.

6

What Are the Limits of Physical Law?

Chapters 3 through 5 describe the quest for new physical laws under circumstances in which it is already known that current understanding is incomplete. What of the familiar laws of physics that human beings use on a regular basis? Particle accelerators and telescopes, and bridges and airplanes, are designed and built through the confident application of principles that have been used and tested over centuries. However, this testing has, for the most part, taken place only under the physical conditions that are accessible to humans working on Earth, and there is an intense curiosity about whether these basic principles of physics are valid under more intense conditions.

The opportunity provided by contemporary astrophysics is to subject essentially all of this "secure" physics to scrutiny in extreme environments, under pressures, temperatures, energies, and densities orders of magnitude greater than those that can be created within a terrestrial laboratory. What makes this opportunity so timely is a new generation of astronomical instruments (made possible by technological advances) that can measure with precision the conditions that exist in the extreme environments found in the universe.

There are two quite separate reasons for carrying out this program. The first is to check the basic assumptions made when analyzing exotic cosmic objects like white dwarfs, neutron stars, and black holes. For example, the wavelengths of the spectral lines that are emitted by common atoms on Earth have been measured with great precision. Do similar atoms orbiting a massive black hole at nearly the speed of light emit at exactly the same wavelengths? Although there is no strong reason today to doubt this assumption, it must be checked: If it did turn out to be false, then much of the current understanding of the evolving universe and its contents would be seriously undermined.

The second reason for subjecting the laws of physics to extreme tests is even more important—it affords us the chance to discover entirely new laws. For example, when Albert Einstein thought hard about the most basic principles of kinematics, not just in the everyday world but at speeds near that of light, he was led to the special theory of relativity, with its bizarre melding of space and time. Later, once particle accelerators were built, it became possible to give particles extremely high energies and thus to show that supposedly fundamental particles like the proton actually had substructure—quarks and gluons. Accelerators gave birth to the whole new field of particle physics, whose laws are so different from those of classical physics. It will be quite remarkable if more "new" physics is not uncovered by probing matter under more extreme conditions.

Fortunately, the approaches to satisfying these twin reasons are identical. The problem must be attacked from both ends on the one hand by using the universe as a giant cosmic laboratory and watching it perform experiments and on the other by carrying out controlled experiments on Earth that are tailored to simulate, as closely as possible, astrophysical conditions. Neither approach by itself is complete. The cosmic laboratory includes the astrophysicist only as a silent witness, a decoder of distant events from fragmentary clues, rather like a historian or an archaeologist. The experimental physicist has more immediate control but cannot recreate the extraordinary range of conditions that occur in the universe. The two approaches are therefore complementary and should be pursued in parallel.

Particle accelerators exist on Earth that can raise protons to energies 1,000 times greater than their energies at rest. Many trillions of particles can be accelerated, from which a few very rare and valuable events are culled. However, for the foreseeable future, building a terrestrial accelerator with sufficient energy to explore directly the unification of all the forces is inconceivable. By contrast, cosmic ray protons are created in distant, astronomical sources with energies some 300 million times greater than those produced by the largest particle accelerators on Earth (see Box 6.1). These collide with atoms in the upper atmosphere, and the products of these collisions are observed on the ground as sprays of particles called air showers. Thus, cosmic ray protons can be used to explore physics at much higher energies, but only with rather primitive diagnostics. Both accelerators and cosmic ray experiments are needed to obtain a complete picture.

EXTREME COSMIC ENVIRONMENTS

Many cosmic environments for testing physical laws are associated with stars or their remnants. The interiors of stars have temperatures of several millions of degrees, hot enough to drive the nuclear reactions that make them shine. When a star's fuel is exhausted, it shrinks under the pull of gravity, becoming even hotter in the process. Relatively small stars like the Sun come to rest as dense white dwarfs—one teaspoon of a white dwarf weighs several tons. Yet this density pales in comparison with that of neutron stars, formed by the spectacular supernova explosions of more massive stars, that have density beyond that of nuclear matter, 1,000 trillion times that of normal matter and initial temperatures of over 100 billion degrees (see Box 6.2). Neutron stars themselves have a maximum mass (less than three solar masses), and the most massive supernovae have no option but to

BOX 6.1   ULTRAHIGH-ENERGY COSMIC RAYS

"Cosmic ray" is the name given to high-energy particles arriving at Earth from space, including protons and nuclei. Of particular interest are the highest-energy particles, whose source is currently unknown. Such particles are so rare that their detection requires huge, many square-kilometer arrays on the ground to collect air showers, the cascades of particles that are created as cosmic rays strike the upper atmosphere. The event rate is so low at the highest energies that it is still not clear whether the spectrum actually shows the predicted high-energy cutoff predicted due to degradation by interactions with the cosmic microwave background radiation (see text). There is some evidence, still not conclusive, that the spectrum of cosmic rays extends past the cutoff energy, at 5×10^{19} eV. The handful of events above this energy are of exceptional interest because of their extraordinarily high energy coupled with the fact that they must come from relatively nearby sources, cosmologically speaking.

Current data indicate that the flux of particles above the cutoff energy is only about five particles per square kilometer per century. The main challenge is therefore simply to collect a sufficiently large sample. Several experiments are under way or proposed to address this problem. Their aim is to discover a characteristic pattern that reveals the nature of the sources. An important technical aspect of all the new experiments is the atmospheric fluorescence technique, by which profiles of individual air showers can be observed from a relatively compact array of telescopes that track the trajectory across the sky—the so-called Fly's Eye technique. The technique can be used alone or in hybrid mode with a giant array of particle detectors on the ground. The ultimate use of this technique would be to monitor huge areas of the atmosphere from space to detect giant cascades. To detect the high-energy neutrinos that may accompany the production of ultrahigh-energy cosmic rays, a large array of detectors deep in water or ice is needed to record the characteristic flashes of light from neutrino interactions while suppressing the background from low-energy cosmic rays that bombard Earth's surface. Some strategies for detecting ultrahigh-energy cosmic rays and neutrinos are illustrated in Figure 6.1.1.

(continued on next page)

BOX 6.1   *(continued)*

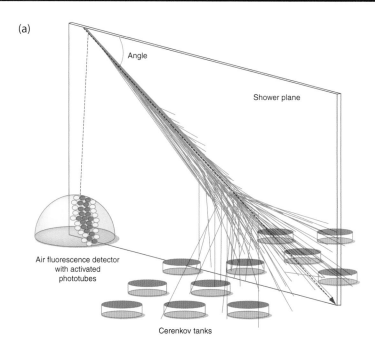

FIGURE 6.1.1   (a) Illustration of a ground-based array of Cerenkov water detectors for detecting shower particles with a fluorescence detector for imaging the atmospheric cascade generated by ultra-high-energy cosmic rays. (b) An array of phototubes suspended in ice that senses interactions of upward-going neutrinos; it uses the bulk of the Earth to filter out other types of particles; adapted from image courtesy of the IceCube Collaboration. (c) One of the Cerenkov shower detectors in the Pierre Auger Observatory array in Argentina; image courtesy of the Pierre Auger Observatory.

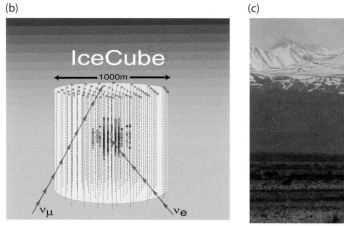

BOX 6.2   NEUTRON STARS AND PULSARS

When a star has exhausted its nuclear fuel, a runaway collapse of the core and ejection of the mantle in a supernova explosion mark its demise. In stars more than about 15 times the mass of the Sun, nothing can arrest the collapse of the core into a black hole. When the initial mass is some 6 to 15 times the solar mass, matter in the core is crushed only to nuclear density and the collapse stops. Electrons and protons combine to make neutrons and neutrinos, the neutrinos escape, and the remnant is a bizarre "nucleus" some 10 km in radius—a neutron star. Following the ejection of the mantle in a supernova, a neutron star is formed. Not all neutron stars have the same mass; many do have well-determined masses of around 1.4 solar masses. A neutron star of mass greater than about 3 solar masses cannot support itself against gravity, and collapse to a black hole is inevitable. Neutron stars are hot, rapidly spinning, highly magnetized objects. Radiation is channeled and emitted in searchlight beams along the magnetic axes. When the spin and magnetic axes are not aligned, the beams rotate rapidly through the sky, giving rise to regular pulses as they briefly illuminate Earth. Such spinning neutron stars are called pulsars.

The neutron star is as exotic an environment as one could wish for (Figure 6.2.1). On the star's surface, a sugar cube would weigh as much as the Great Pyramid of Egypt. The surface is most likely made of metallic iron. Below, the pressure increases rapidly, and electrons are captured by protons to make increasingly neutron-rich nuclei. The nuclei become large droplets and take on strange shapes—strings, sheets, and tubes. This region, down to a depth of about 1 km, is whimsically known as the "pasta" regime. Below that, there are mostly neutrons, with a few protons and electrons. But the pressure continues to grow with depth, and it is possible that some of the electrons may be replaced by heavier particles called pions or kaons, which can combine into a collective state called a condensate. Finally it is likely that a quark-gluon plasma may form at several times nuclear density at the very center.

The response of nuclear matter to these incredible pressures is not well understood. Measurements of the masses, radii, and surface temperatures of neutron stars provide a window onto their interiors and reveal much about how nuclear forces behave under extreme conditions.

Magnetosphere
Superhot plasma

Outer Crust
Crystal lattice: 200 meters deep
nuclei + electrons

Inner Crust
Crystal lattice: 1 km deep
nuclei + electrons + neutron gas

Outer Core
Neutron, proton, and electron fluid

Inner Core
Meson condensates, quark droplets,
bulk quark matter?

20 kilometers
(12 mi) diameter

FIGURE 6.2.1   Schematic of the interior of a neutron star showing the layers of packed and compressed matter. Condensed matter physics can tell us many things about the forms that matter takes, except at the very center of the neutron star, where densities exceed those of nuclear matter.

collapse all the way to infinite density, forming black holes (see Box 6.3). Such collapses may also trigger a gamma-ray burst—an explosive burst of gamma rays lasting only a few seconds but with an apparent power that may for a brief instant approach the power of the entire visible universe. The pressures inside these sources may exceed a trillion trillion atmospheres, comparable to the pressure encountered in the expanding universe when it was only about 10 milliseconds old. (By contrast, the most powerful lasers for creating astrophysical conditions can only create pressures of about a billion trillion atmospheres.)

Far from marking the permanent death of a star, any of these compact objects may herald its rebirth in a more active form. This may happen, for example, if a remnant has a regular star as a binary companion and the star swells and dumps its gas onto the compact object. The gas may swirl around the compact object for a time on its way down, forming a hot accretion disk, moving with a speed approaching that of light, and emitting x rays, or it may settle onto the surface of the compact object, providing fresh fuel for nuclear explosions. Young, rapidly spinning neutron stars called pulsars can radiate very intense radio and gamma-ray radiation (see Box 6.2). Their power derives from the spin of the neutron star, which has a magnetic field over a million times larger than can be sustained on Earth and which acts like a giant electrical generator capable of producing over 1,000 trillion volts and more than 10 trillion amperes. Other pulsars are powered by gravity, through their accretion of matter from a nearby companion.

Even larger black holes are found in the nuclei of galaxies. Essentially all galaxies, including our own, harbor in their centers black holes with masses between a million and billion times that of the Sun. These black holes are the engines for the hyperactive galactic nuclei called quasars, which for a time in the early universe outshone whole galaxies by up to a thousandfold. Quasars, too, are powered by accretion disks, fueled by gas supplied by their host galaxies. In addition, they often form "jets"—moving beams of high-energy particles and magnetic fields—which radiate across the whole spectrum from the longest radio waves to the highest-energy gamma-rays. It appears that these jets are formed very close to the central black hole, but understanding in detail how they are formed remains a major puzzle.

One of the most intriguing questions involves cosmic rays, mentioned above. It is believed that cosmic rays are energized by the shock waves associated with cosmic explosions like supernovae. However, this explanation is challenged to account for the fastest particles, with individual

BOX 6.3   BLACK HOLES

Any object whose radius becomes smaller than a certain value (called the Schwarzschild radius) is doomed to collapse to a singularity of infinite density. No known force of nature can overcome this collapse. The Schwarzschild radius (or event horizon) is proportional to the object's mass and corresponds to that distance where even light cannot escape the gravitational pull of the central matter. Because of this property, these collapsed singularities are called black holes. Just outside the Schwarzschild radius, outwardly traveling photons can barely escape to infinity. It has even been speculated that there could be "naked singularities," which are not shrouded by an event horizon.

Properly describing the geometry of space-time (which dictates the motion of both particles and light) near a black hole requires Einstein's theory of general relativity. Particle as well as light trajectories become severely distorted, or curved, compared with those predicted by the Newtonian description. Geometrically, space near a black hole can be exactly described by simple formulae, the Kerr solutions to Einstein's equations. The gravitational field depends on only two parameters, the mass and spin of the hole. The radius of the event horizon and the smallest orbit that matter can have without falling in depend on how fast the hole is spinning—the faster the spin, the closer material can get.

Einstein's theory of general relativity is only just now beginning to be tested (e.g., by measurements made by the Rossi X-ray Timing Experiment) in regions of strong gravity, where gravitational forces accelerate matter to speeds close to the speed of light. The most straightforward test would be to observe matter directly as it swirls into a black hole, measuring the particle trajectories and comparing them with the predictions of theory. This may be possible someday with the extremely high resolution achievable with x-ray interferometers. However, nature has provided an indirect tracer of black holes at the centers of galaxies that is already being exploited. As heavy elements like iron spiral inward toward a black hole, they reach high orbital velocities and temperatures in the tens of millions of degrees. Transitions of electrons between discrete atomic energy levels generate radiation of specific wavelengths that can be observed in the x-ray band. The wavelengths of these spectral lines are altered by several effects: a Doppler shift due to each atom's orbital velocity around the hole (the shift can be positive or negative, depending on whether the motion is toward or away from the observer); an overall shift to longer wavelengths that occurs for all radiation struggling to escape from black holes; and another longward shift due to the time-dilating effects of high-speed motion near the hole. The net result is that the lines are shifted and broadened, with "wings" whose shape depends on the atoms' trajectories as determined by the geometry of space-time. Recent observations of broad lines from the nuclei of active galaxies believed to contain massive black holes are consistent with solutions in which the black hole is spinning rapidly.

energies comparable to that of a well-hit baseball; it may be that scientists are seeing evidence for completely new forms of matter. Very-high-energy neutrinos, some of which may be produced by jets, can also be created, and experiments are on the threshold of being able to detect these, too.

Finally, the most penetrating signals of all are gravitational waves, first predicted by Einstein in 1918 (see Box 6.4). Scientists know that these waves really do exist because the energy they carry off into space affects the orbits of binary pulsars in a manner that matches well with precision measurements of observed binary pulsar systems. However, they have not yet been detected directly. The most promising sources of gravitational waves, which involve the collisions and coalescences of large black holes, are even more luminous than gamma-ray bursts.

NEW CHALLENGES IN EXTREME ASTROPHYSICS

Four problem areas, drawn from the physics-astronomy interface, are ready for a concerted attack.

Black Holes and Strong Gravity

Isaac Newton's theory of gravity has been superseded by Albert Einstein's general theory of relativity, which is widely believed to be the "true" theory of gravity as long as quantum mechanical corrections are unimportant. The subtle differences between Newton's and Einstein's theories have been tested in the solar system by monitoring the motions of the Moon, the planets, and light. So far general relativity has passed every test with a quantitative precision that in several cases exceeds 1 part in a 1,000. Outside the solar system, the first binary pulsar, PSR1913+16, provided a test in stronger fields. By monitoring the arrival time of regular radio pulses from this source, it was possible to measure the orbital decay caused by the power lost as the two orbiting neutron stars radiated gravitational radiation. Theory and observation agree within about 3 parts per 1,000. The tests of general relativity have been so significant that few scientists doubt its validity in the regimes probed.

However, in both the solar system and pulsar tests, gravity is still relatively weak in the sense that the characteristic speeds of bodies are less than roughly one-thousandth the speed of light. Therefore the critical limit of the theory in which objects move at near-light speeds has not yet been tested. It is a basic tenet of physics that, if a physical law is truly understood and has been verified to very high accuracy in at least one location, it should be

BOX 6.4   GRAVITATIONAL RADIATION AND GRAVITY-WAVE DETECTORS

The general theory of relativity posits that matter (and energy) introduces curvature into four-dimensional space-time and that matter moves in response to this curvature. The theory admits wave solutions in which gravitational ripples in the fabric of space-time propagate with the speed of light. Such waves are an inescapable consequence of general relativity (and indeed of most theories of gravity). However, there are also some very important differences from electromagnetic radiation. Electromagnetic waves accelerate individual charged particles, and this property underlies their detection in, for example, radio antennas. Similarly, gravitational waves are detected by measuring the relative acceleration induced between a pair of test masses as the wave passes by. In addition, when gravitational wave amplitudes are large, as in some cosmic sources, the wave energy of gravitational radiation *itself* becomes a source of gravity, which is not true for electromagnetic waves. This nonlinearity complicates the theory of wave generation, necessitating extensive numerical computation to calculate the expected wave intensity from a given source.

The best-understood sources of gravitational radiation are binary stars. Two white dwarfs or neutron stars in close orbit lose energy via gravitational radiation and spiral in toward each other. A good example is the first binary pulsar discovered, PSR 1913+16, which comprises two neutron stars in an 8-hour orbit. One of these neutron stars emits a radio pulse every 59 milliseconds, and by monitoring very accurately the arrival times of these pulses at Earth, radio astronomers have followed the inspiral and consequent change of orbital period. As the speeds of these neutron stars are much less than the speed of light, it is possible to compute their orbits very accurately. The measurement agrees with general relativity to a precision of 3 parts per 1,000 and effectively rules out most other theories. So, in a sense, researchers have already verified the existence of gravitational waves.

Testing the theory when gravity is strong requires measuring gravitational waves directly. There are several likely strong sources of gravitational radiation: inspiraling binary neutron stars, supernova explosions, and merging supermassive black holes in galactic nuclei. In all cases, the goal is to measure the gravitational wave profile as the mass falls together and compare it with nonlinear predictions using general relativity. A peculiarly relativistic effect called Lense-Thirring precession arises when space is "dragged" by the spinning black hole. Measuring this effect would also indicate how rapidly black holes spin. In general, if the comparison between observation and theory is successful, it will constitute an impressive validation of the fundamental theory of gravity.

More exotic sources of gravitational radiation have also been proposed. A particularly important one is primordial gravity waves generated soon after the big bang in the early universe. One particular epoch proposed is that in which quarks changed into ordinary nucleons, the so-called quark-hadron transition. If this happened abruptly, in a manner similar to that by which water changes into steam, then the gravity-wave intensity may be detectable. Other such phase transitions in the early universe associated

(continued on next page)

BOX 6.4   *(continued)*

FIGURE 6.4.1   Aerial photographs of the interferometers used in the Laser Inteferometrer Gravitational Wave Observatory (LIGO). The long tunnels house the evacuated laser chambers, in which laser beams travel a 4-km path length. At the vertex of the L, and at the end of each of its arms, are test masses that hang from wires and that are outfitted with mirrors. Ultrastable laser beams traversing the vacuum pipes are used to detect the ultrasmall change in the separation of a pair of test masses caused by the passage of a gravitational wave. Images courtesy of the LIGO Laboratory.

with the unification of the forces have also been discussed. Inflation is perhaps the most compelling source of gravitational waves from the early universe. Detection of gravity waves from the early universe would allow us to look back at extremely early times and to study physics that is simply not accessible in a terrestrial lab.

Two distinct types of classical gravitational wave detector have been proposed. The first is a ground-based laser interferometer designed to measure tiny changes in the separations of pairs of test masses (suspended by wires) due to the passage of gravitational waves. A prominent example is the Laser Interferometer Gravitational Wave Observatory (LIGO), which comprises two sites (for redundancy), one in Washington state and the other in Louisiana (Figure 6.4.1). At each site, three test masses are spaced 4 kilometers apart; it is hoped eventually to measure relative displacements between the masses as small as 10^{-19} meters. This facility, which began operation in 2002, will be especially sensitive to waves with periods in the range from 3 to 100 milliseconds and is therefore tuned to collapsing sources of stellar mass. To detect the gravitational radiation from the formation of more massive black holes, a larger detector that is sensitive to lower frequencies is required. Because of natural size limitations as well as seismic noise, such a detector would have to be deployed in space. Studies for a space-based gravitational wave detector to complement LIGO are under way in the United States and in Europe (see Figures 6.4.2 and 6.4.3).

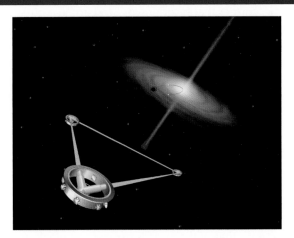

FIGURE 6.4.2   An artist's sketch for the Laser Interferometer Space Array (LISA) as it might look. Laser beams bounce back and forth between the apices of the triangle formed by the three satellites, using the same principles as the ground-based LIGO. Image courtesy of the Jet Propulsion Laboratory, California Institute of Technology, Pasadena, California.

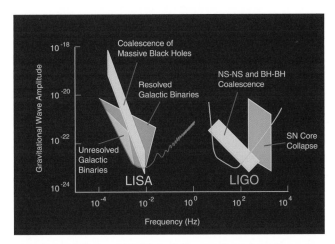

FIGURE 6.4.3   A comparison of the sensitivities of the two laser interferometer projects (LIGO and LISA) to gravitational waves of different frequencies. Different sources of gravity waves are expected to produce waves of different kinds; the LIGO and LISA project are expected to complement each other to cover a broader range of the gravity wave spectrum. Figure courtesy of the Jet Propulsion Laboratory, California Institute of Technology, Pasadena, California.

possible to use it anywhere it is claimed to be valid. Thus, if general relativity is the correct theory of gravity, researchers already know what should happen when the field is strong, even though they have not tested it there yet. However, it is conceivable that general relativity may not be a comprehensive theory of gravity. Moreover, one of its most impressive predictions, the existence of cosmic points of no return—black holes—has not been fully tested. It is therefore imperative to test relativity where gravity is strong. There is no better cosmic laboratory than a black hole (see Box 6.3).

It is now clear beyond all reasonable doubt that black holes are abundant in the universe. They appear to be present in the nuclei of most regular galaxies and to have masses ranging from millions to billions times that of the Sun. In addition, much smaller black holes (5 to 15 solar masses) are being found, commonly in x-ray binary star systems in our galaxy. Recent evidence suggests a class of black holes with masses between 30 and a million times that of the Sun. Astrophysical black holes are defined by two parameters: (1) mass, which sets the size of the black-hole space-time and (2) spin, which determines the detailed geometry of the black-hole space-time. Spin is important because, as noted in the case of pulsars, rotational energy provides a reservoir of extractable energy rather like a giant flywheel, and it can act as a prime mover for much of the dramatic high-energy emission associated with black holes.

Observational knowledge of black holes has advanced remarkably in the last 5 years. Masses have been measured with increasing precision, and scientists are starting to understand how the sizes of black holes relate to their host galaxies or stellar companions. In addition, at least two approaches to measuring black hole spins appear to be promising, although they are yet to be convincingly exploited. Massive holes in galactic nuclei are often orbited by accretion disks of gas that spiral inward, eventually crossing the event horizon—the surface from which nothing, not even light, can escape.

The spectral lines from atoms such as iron orbiting the black hole are quite broad because they are subjected to a variable Doppler shift relative to an Earth-based observer. They are also shifted to lower energy because photons lose energy in climbing out of the hole's deep potential well. It turns out that gas can remain close to the black hole *and* produce such a strongly broadened and redshifted line only if the hole spins nearly as fast as possible. On this basis, at least some active galactic nucleus black holes are already thought to rotate very rapidly.

It may be possible to use x-ray flares to map out the immediate environments of black holes only light-hours from their centers. This technique makes use of the fact that it takes a finite amount of time for high-energy x rays from the flare to travel to the disk and excite iron emission; different parts of the disk will therefore be observed at different times, allowing the space-time around the black hole to be probed. Alternatively, if astronomers are lucky enough to catch one, a star in orbit around a black hole could also provide a powerful probe of the space-time as it is drawn in and torn apart.

There is a serious obstacle to carrying out this program. The wavelengths and the strengths of all of the spectral lines emitted by the accretion disks, which are at very high temperatures, are simply not known. (In fact it is not yet possible to identify half of the lines in the solar spectrum.) Although the quantum mechanical principles necessary to calculate these effects are understood, the atoms are so complex in practice that it is necessary to mount a focused program in experimental laboratory astrophysics to make the most of existing observations of accretion disks.

A second approach to measuring a black hole's spin comes from monitoring the rapid quasi-periodic oscillations of the x-ray intensity from selected galactic binary sources. These are almost certainly influenced by both the strong deviations from Newtonian gravity that are present close to the event horizon, independent of the spin, and a peculiarly spin-dependent effect called the dragging of inertial frames (see Figure 6.1). Frame-dragging requires that all matter must follow the black hole's spin close to the event horizon. In addition, if the matter follows an orbit that is inclined with respect to the black hole's spin, the orbit plane must rapidly precess. Both effects change the oscillation frequencies. Although it has been argued that

FIGURE 6.1   Frame dragging near a massive, rotating black hole. All matter must follow the black hole's spin when it gets very close to the event horizon. Image courtesy of Joe Bergeron ©2001, <www.joebergeron.com>.

the consequences of both of these effects are already being observed (e.g., in quasiperiodic oscillations seen in neutron star accretion disks), neither approach is understood well enough to allow confidence that it is the spins that are being measured, let alone testing general relativity.

An even bigger challenge is to image a black hole directly. Two ambitious approaches are currently under investigation. The first involves constructing a spaceborne x-ray interferometer to resolve the x-ray-emitting gas orbiting the black hole. By combining beams from x-ray telescopes far apart, it is possible in principle to produce images with microarcsecond angular resolution—300,000 times better than the best optical mirrors in space. This resolution is sufficient to enable seeing the event horizon of a supermassive black hole in the nucleus of a nearby galaxy. A second method involves submillimeter-wave interferometry, perhaps also prosecuted from space. This approach is useful for observing sources like our own galactic center, which, although not a powerful x-ray source, does emit submillimeter radiation bright enough to permit resolving the radio source that envelops the central black hole.

A quite different and more comprehensive approach to testing general relativity is to measure directly the gravitational radiation emitted by a pair of merging compact objects. Ground-based facilities in Louisiana and Washington, the Laser Interferometric Gravitational Wave Observatory (LIGO), are designed to detect merging stellar-mass compact objects in nearby galaxies. To measure gravitational radiation from forming or merging massive (or intermediate-mass) black holes, it will be necessary to construct a facility in space. Nearly as difficult as building these observatories, however, is the task of computing the gravitational waveforms that are expected when two black holes merge. This is a major challenge in computational general relativity and one that will stretch computational hardware and software to the limits. However, a bonus is that the waveforms will be quite unique to general relativity, and if they are reproduced observationally, scientists will have performed a highly sensitive test of gravity in the strong-field regime.

Finally, neutron stars also provide an astrophysical laboratory for testing the predictions of general relativity in strong gravitational fields. The quasiperiodic oscillations (QPOs) seen in association with the accretion of material onto neutron stars may be useful in probing effects predicted by general relativity, such as Lense-Thirring precession.

Neutron Stars as Giant Atomic Nuclei

Atomic nuclei are held together by nuclear forces. At the simplest level these forces act between protons and neutrons, but at a more fundamental level they involve their constituent quarks and are mediated by the carriers of the strong force, the gluons. The gross structure of natural nuclei is comparatively well understood (with some conspicuous problems remaining, e.g., understanding the effect of the underlying quark structure on nuclei), because it is fairly well understood how nucleons interact when they are about 2 femtometers (10^{-15} m) apart, as they are in normal nuclei. However, what happens when matter is compressed to greater baryon density or heated to a higher temperature?

To address this question, a major facility, the Relativistic Heavy Ion Collider (RHIC), has been constructed at Brookhaven National Laboratory. Using this facility, it will be possible to collide heavy nuclei, like gold, so that they momentarily attain a density roughly 10 times that of nuclear matter. Under these circumstances, it may be possible to form a quark-gluon plasma—a denser version of the state of matter that is thought to have existed in the universe earlier than about 10 microseconds after the big bang. A strong experimental program at RHIC will be carried out over the next few years to see what the states of matter are at extreme energy density.

Nature has performed a complementary experiment by making neutron stars in supernova explosions. Neutron stars are about one and a half times as massive as the Sun and have radii of about 10 km. They can be considered as giant nuclei, containing roughly 10^{57} nucleons with an average density similar to that of normal nuclei. However, as gravity provides an additional strong attractive force, the densities at the *centers* of neutron stars are almost certainly well above nuclear, as in the heavy ion collisions. There is one crucial and important difference between colliding heavy ions and neutron stars. In the former case, the dense nuclear matter is extremely hot, about 10^{12} K, whereas neutron stars usually have temperatures of less than 10^9 K, which from a nuclear standpoint is cold. Scientists are still quite unsure about the properties of cold matter at densities well above nuclear matter density.

One good way to see what really happens is to measure the masses and radii of neutron stars with high precision. The masses of a handful are known to exquisite precision (1 part in 10,000), and a number of others are known to within a few percent, from the study of their binary orbits. Promising ways to measure neutron star radii involve high-resolution x-ray spectroscopy or the study of so-called quasi-periodic oscillations. The most direct approach is to observe the wavelengths and shapes of spectral lines formed within a hot neutron star atmosphere immediately following a thermonuclear explosion beneath the star's surface. (These explosions, called x-ray bursts, are commonly observed from neutron stars that are fed with gaseous fuel at a high rate.) The central wavelengths of the x-ray lines provide a measurement of the gravitational redshift—essentially the depth of the gravitational potential well—and the widths and strengths of the lines measure the rotation speed near the neutron star's surface. Together with a good understanding of the neutron star atmosphere, these two quantities fix the mass and the radius. In addition, if the distance to the neutron star is known, it is possible to estimate the radius yet another way by knowing that the observed flux strength varies in proportion to the surface area of the star (although one must assume that the entire star is being observed). Given an accurate determination of the radius of a neutron star of known mass, it will be possible to constrain the compressibility of cold nuclear matter and thus the nature of its underlying composition and particle interactions.

An even more direct approach to learning the composition of highly compressed nuclear matter involves neutron star cooling. Neutron stars are born hot inside supernovae, which also create shells of expanding debris known as supernova remnants (see Figures 6.2 and 6.3). The size of this remnant is a measure of the neutron star's age, and the star itself yields its surface temperature. New theories in condensed matter physics can then be used to relate the surface temperature to the temperature inside. In sum, by observing neutron stars of different ages, astronomers can measure how fast they cool.

It turns out that if the interior of a neutron star contains just neutrons and a small fraction of protons and electrons, it ought to cool quite slowly, but if it contains a significant fraction of protons or other particles like pions or kaons or even free quarks, it will cool much more quickly. Thus it is possible to learn about a neutron star's interior simply by measuring its surface temperature. In addition, neutron star interiors are believed to be in a superfluid state, with their protons superconducting, and this too would influence the cooling. Neutron stars can serve as excellent cosmic laboratories for testing physical ideas in this new territory.

As explained in Chapter 2, quantum electrodynamics (QED) is a highly quantitative quantum theory of the electromagnetic interaction of photons and matter. It makes predictions that have been tested with great precision in regimes accessible to laboratory study. In particular, it has been tested in static magnetic fields as large as roughly 10^5 G.

However, ever since the discovery of pulsars, it has been known that fields as large as 10^{12} G are commonly found on the surfaces of neutron stars. More recently it has been concluded that a subset of neutron stars, called "magnetars," have magnetic field strengths of 10^{14} to 10^{15} G, well above the QED "critical" field, where the kinetic energy of an electron spiraling in the magnetic field exceeds its rest mass energy. QED should still be a correct description above this critical field, but the physics is quite different from what is normally considered. For example, when an x ray propagates through a vacuum endowed with a strong magnetic field, QED predicts that electron-positron pairs will be created in such a way that the emergent x-ray radiation will become polarized. It may therefore be possible to observe QED at work in magnetars by observing x-ray polarization and mapping out the neutron star magnetic field. Measuring x-ray polarization is difficult, but, encouragingly, it has recently become possible to measure the circular polarization of x rays from laboratory synchrotrons. Perhaps these techniques can also be used in space x-ray observatories.

Supernova Explosions and the Origin of the Heavy Elements

The big bang produced the lightest elements in the periodic table—hydrogen, helium, and lithium. Planets and people are made not only of these elements but also of carbon, nitrogen, oxygen, iron, and all the other elements in the periodic table. It is believed that the elements beyond lithium are made in the contemporary universe by stars and stellar explosions. There is a good understanding of the origin of elements up to the iron group (nickel, cobalt, and iron). The iron-group elements have the greatest binding energies, so the elements up to the iron group can be made by nuclear reactions that fuse two nuclei to make a heavier nucleus and release energy. However, producing the elements heavier than iron requires energy input, and astrophysicists have looked to stellar explosions as the likely production sites. The details of how the heaviest elements are made are still not fully known.

Supernovae mark the violent deaths of the most massive main-sequence stars and also of close binaries with one highly condensed member (e.g., a white dwarf). These cataclysmic explosions, which can be seen far across the cosmos, can be used as markers of time and distance (see Figure 5.7 for a gallery). Supernovae occur because stars become unstable either as they evolve or as they accrete matter. A main-sequence star of several solar masses can produce energy by successively combining elements up to iron. After nuclear burning has turned the core to iron-group elements, no more energy can be produced. This impasse triggers the collapse of the core and the explosion of the mantle in a supernova. Thermonuclear runaway also occurs when a white dwarf accretes too much mass from a main-sequence companion.

(a)

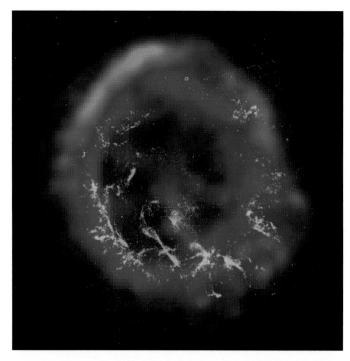

FIGURE 6.2 False-color images of the shock-heated x-ray glowing gas surrounding four supernova remnants: (a) SN0102-72 (image courtesy of NASA/CXC/SAO, HST, CSIRO/ATNE/ATCA), (b) G11.2-0.3 (image courtesy of NASA/McGill, V. Kaspi et al.), (c) Cassiopeia A (image courtesy of NASA/CXC/CSAO), and (d) N132D (image courtesy of NASA/SAO/CXC).

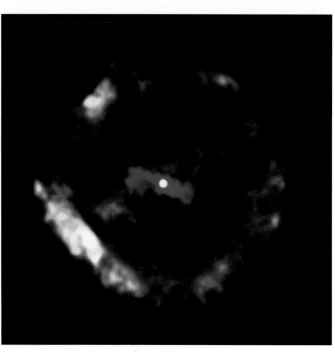

(b)

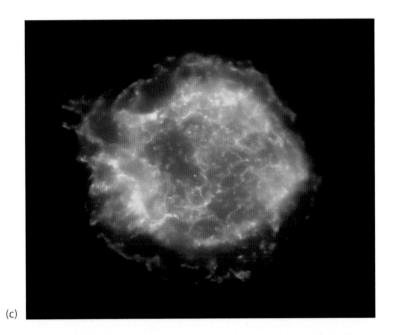

(c)

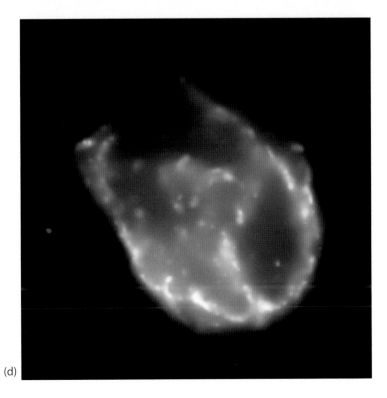

(d)

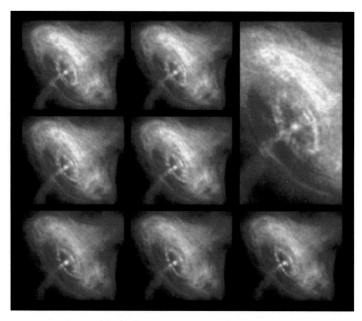

FIGURE 6.3   Time-lapse, false-color x-ray images of the hot spinning disk of gas surrounding the neutron star with the Crab Nebula taken by the Chandra X-ray Observatory over the course of several months. Image courtesy of NASA/CXC/ASU/J. Hester et al.

Supernovae are classified theoretically by mechanism—core collapse or accretion—and observationally by whether hydrogen is present in the ejecta. Type I supernovae lack hydrogen, while Type II do not. (The categories are further subdivided into Ia, Ib, Ic, II-P, II-L, II-n, and IIb according to the pattern of heavy elements ejected.) The two means of classification do not necessarily coincide, and we lack a detailed theoretical understanding of how to make the correspondence. Nevertheless, Type Ia supernovae are observed to have very similar intrinsic luminosities and have provided convincing evidence that the expansion of the universe is speeding up (see Chapter 5). Discovering whether Type Ia supernovae are truly a homogeneous class and learning what spread is to be expected in their properties are high-priority objectives of supernova research.

Supernovae are clearly the factories in which the elements up to and slightly above the iron group of elements are made. Not only are the detailed abundances of the elements lighter than iron quantitatively understood with the aid of nuclear theory and laboratory data, but the telltale signatures of radioactive isotopes also are seen in the expanding shell of debris following a supernova explosion.

When it comes to understanding the origin of elements much heaver than iron, however, scientists can reconstruct much of what must have happened, but the astrophysical factory has not been clearly identified. Intermediate-mass elements are made in a neutron-rich environment in which successive neutron captures occur slowly, and neutron-rich nuclei undergo beta decay back to more stable elements. Still heavier nuclei must have been made by a succession of rapid neutron captures, referred to as the r-process. A dense, highly neutron-rich environment must exist for the r-process to occur. Also seen in the abundances are the traces of other mechanisms, including possible evidence of nucleosynthesis induced by neutrinos. The element fluorine, for example, can be made by neutrinos interacting with supernova debris. In fact, it is strongly suspected that supernovae, once again, must be the place where the remaining elements up to uranium are built, but there is no detailed understanding of how the process occurs. Resolving this problem requires observational data from supernova remnants, experimental data from both nuclear physics and neutrino physics, and the ability to make detailed, fully three-dimensional, theoretical calculations of supernova explosions.

To begin with, theoretical models of supernovae are still incomplete. Simply producing a reliable "explosion" (in the computer) has proven to be an enormous challenge. Recently, the importance of convection driven by neutrino heating from the nascent neutron-star core was confirmed by numerical calculations. The key was to do calculations in two dimensions instead of one (convection in one dimension is impossible). However, not until it is possible to do a full three-dimensional calculation with full and complete physics will the combined role of rotation and convection be clear. A full three-dimensional calculation with proper inclusion of neutrino transport will require the terascale computing facilities that are just now being realized. There is reason to hope that such a calculation will distinguish the site of the r-process and at the same time illustrate the properties neutrinos must have to match what is currently known about the elements, resolving with a single stroke two important questions in modern physics.

To make this step in computational prowess, however, theory will call upon experiment to provide solid ground for the r-process. In equal measure, progress will come from measurements in neutrino physics and in nuclear physics. Neutrino oscillations can dramatically alter the synthesis of the elements in a supernova, because the muon and tau neutrinos made in a supernova are much hotter (more energetic) than the electron neutrinos. Normally neutrino effects are muted because muon and tau neutrinos do not interact so easily with nuclei, while electron neutrinos are not produced so hot. But if oscillations scramble the identities, the hot muon and tau neutrinos can turn into hot electron neutrinos and readily disintegrate nuclei just built by the r-process.

The nuclei built in rapid neutron capture lie at the boundary of nuclear stability, the neutron "drip line." To trace the path of nucleosynthesis, researchers need to know the masses and lifetimes of nuclei far from the ones that can be reached with existing technology. The binding energy of such exotic nuclei can be calculated well for nuclei nearer the "valley of stability" (the region in the diagram of all possible nuclei described by their numbers of neutrons and protons where the most stable nuclei are found). How well those equations serve in extrapolation to r-process nuclei is completely unknown. In the last few years it has been realized that these nuclei can be produced and measured in a two-stage acceleration, isotope-production, re-acceleration facility. With a suitably designed facility, every r-process nucleus may be accessible for direct measurement.

Finally, there will be in the coming decades the opportunity to observe directly the synthesis of heavy elements where it is believed that synthesis occurs—that is, in the explosions of stars. These explosions create radioactive nuclei, which decay over time, usually with the emission of a gamma ray of specific energy. Future sensitive high-energy x-ray and gamma-ray space experiments will allow these decays to be observed and monitored over time soon after the explosion and the distribution of newly synthesized material in the remnant matter expelled in the explosion to be mapped with high fidelity. These remnants can "glow" for tens of thousands of years in observable radiation. Such observations can be used to constrain the theoretical models for the explosions, directly measure the quantities of synthesized material, and observe how it gets distributed into the space between stars.

Cosmic Accelerators and High-Energy Physics

Earth is continuously bombarded by relativistic particles called cosmic rays, which are known to originate beyond the solar system. Cosmic rays with energies up to at least 10^{14} eV are probably accelerated at the shock fronts associated with supernova explosions, and radio emissions and x rays give direct evidence that electrons are accelerated there to nearly the speed of light. However, the evidence that high-energy cosmic-ray protons and nuclei have a supernova origin is only circumstantial and needs confirmation. Most puzzling are the much higher energy cosmic rays with energies as large as 3×10^{20} eV. In fact, it would seem that they ought not to exist at all, because traveling through the sea of CMB photons for longer than roughly 100 million years would rob them of their ultrahigh energy.

Accounting for these particles—probably mostly protons—is one of the greatest challenges in high-energy astrophysics. Among the many suggested origins are nearby active galactic nuclei, gamma-ray bursts, and the decay of topological defects or other massive relics of the big bang.

Protons are not the only type of ultrahigh-energy particle that might be observed from these sources—many models also imply the associated production of high-energy neutrinos. In models involving decaying massive particle relics from the big bang, such neutrinos would emerge from cascades of decaying quarks and gluons that set in at the energy scale of grand unification. In models involving particle acceleration, they could be produced in interactions of protons with dense photon fields or gas near the emitting object. The ability to detect high-energy neutrinos from energetic astrophysical sources would open an entirely new window onto the high-energy universe. In particular, since most sources are relatively transparent to their own neutrinos, these particles allow "seeing" the particle acceleration mechanism directly, deep inside the source.

Studying neutrinos is difficult because they interact only through the weak force, so they usually pass through detectors without leaving a trace. One technique for achieving a large effective volume is to detect upward-moving muons created by neutrinos interacting in the material below the sensitive volume of the detector. Upward trajectories guarantee that the parent particles must be neutrinos, because no other particles can penetrate the whole of the Earth. The atmospheric neutrinos, whose behavior provides the current evidence that neutrinos have mass, are detected in a similar way, through their interactions with detectors in deep mines; so far, however, only upper limits have been achieved up to now for energetic astrophysical neutrinos.

Gamma-ray photons, a third type of high-energy particle, have been observed from the cosmos with energies as high as 50 TeV. As is the case for the high-energy cosmic rays, the sources of such energetic photons must all be relatively local on a cosmological scale, since photons of this energy also tend to be destroyed in traveling through space by combining with background infrared photons from starlight to create electron-positron pairs. Many of the highest-energy gamma rays are probably emitted as a by-product of the acceleration of the mysterious ultrahigh-energy cosmic rays. Whether they are produced in cascades initiated by high-energy protons or radiated by electrons could in principle be decided by determining whether or not the high-energy gamma rays are accompanied by neutrinos, a frequent by-product of high-energy proton collisions.

Understanding the origin of the highest-energy particles will require better understanding of the sites where they are accelerated. Gamma-ray bursts produce flashes of high-energy photons, and theory predicts that very-high-energy neutrinos and cosmic rays will accompany the flash. Although significant progress in locating and studying gamma-ray bursts has been made recently, the sources of these enormous explosions is still a matter of debate. Another class of energetic sources, the highly variable but long-lived jets of active galactic nuclei, in some cases emit gamma rays with energies as high as 10 TeV, which directly implies the presence of charged particles of at least this energy. Although quite different in origin, both jets and gamma-ray bursts are thought to involve highly relativistic bulk motion, ultimately powered by accretion onto massive black holes. Scientists only have quite speculative theories to offer at this stage, but future observations, in particular of high-energy radiation, can provide important constraints.

To date, much of the information about powerful cosmic accelerators has come from gamma-ray photons of all energies. Much more information may come from measuring the primary accelerated particles, as well as secondary photons and neutrinos. For example, the observation of a coincident gamma-ray and high-energy neutrino signal from a gamma-ray burst would directly test the existing theories of the shock mechanism in these sources. Identifying accelerated cosmic rays from a particular source is difficult, because intervening magnetic fields scramble the directions of charged particles as they travel. So far, it has only been possible to identify particles coming from solar flares. In contrast, neutrinos and photons, being neutral, are undeflected by magnetic fields and thus can be traced back to individual sources, provided they are bright enough. With projects currently under way or proposed, the ultimate goal of detecting high-energy protons, photons, and neutrinos from specific energetic sources may be within reach.

At the highest energies, it may be possible to identify and study cosmic accelerators by backtracking to the accelerated protons themselves. This is possible because the amount of bending in a given magnetic field is inversely proportional to the energy of the particle, and the highest-energy particles must come from relatively nearby sources to avoid having been degraded by interaction with photons of the microwave background. The aim is to accumulate enough events so that the pattern of their arrival directions and energies will reveal the identity of the specific sources. Ultimately, the highest-energy cascades would be studied from space with detectors able to view a huge section of the atmosphere from above and thus overcome the extremely low occurrence rate of the highest-energy events. "Shower" detectors that view a sufficiently large volume of the atmosphere can also detect ultrahigh-energy neutrinos, which can make horizontal cascades starting deep in the atmosphere or even in the crust of Earth.

Further understanding of the conditions within ultrahigh-energy sources may also come from measurements made on Earth. Although the conditions within these sources cannot be reproduced here in the laboratory, the behavior of bulk matter under unexplored regimes of pressure and temperature can be examined using high-performance lasers. It is already possible to sustain pressures of 10 million atmospheres and magnetic field strengths of 10 megagauss and to create, impulsively, electron-positron pair plasmas with relativistic temperature at these facilities. These investigations are valuable because they provide a much stronger basis for scaling from the laboratory to cosmic sources. They can be particularly useful for understanding giant planets, the dynamics of various types of supernova explosions, and the relativistic flows and shock waves associated with quasars and gamma-ray bursts.

NEW OPPORTUNITIES

It is possible to summarize the discussion above in the form of five fundamental questions that cut across the problem areas discussed as well as the issues identified in the previous chapters.

Did Einstein Have the Last Word on Gravity?

There is a striking opportunity to begin testing general relativity in the strong-field regime using observations of astrophysical black holes. Observations of disks and outflows would test the form of the standard Kerr geometry of a spinning black hole; those of coalescing black holes would test a far more intricate dynamical space-time. The needed observations include x-ray line Doppler shifts and linewidths from black holes, quasi-periodic fluctuations of x-ray intensity from oscillating accretion disks, and gravitational radiation from mergers of compact objects.

What Are the New States of Matter at Exceedingly High Density and Temperature?

Understanding the equation of state and phase transitions of dense nuclear matter is one of the great challenges in contemporary many-body physics. Cold neutron stars and hot supernova explosions provide two quite different ways to obtain unique experimental data and to test theoretical understanding. The opportunities include (1) measuring neutron-star radii from x-ray line gravitational redshifts and from absolute distance and x-ray intensity measurements, neutron-star rotation speeds from x-ray linewidths, x-ray timing measurements from quasi-perioidic oscillations, and the cooling rate of neutron stars in expanding supernova remnants and (2) theoretical work on the nuclear equation of state and the transition between nuclear matter and the quark-gluon plasma (see Figure 6.4).

Is a New Theory of Matter and Light Needed at the Highest Energies?

The committee believes that QED is the most successful theory of physics and that there is, as yet, no good reason to doubt it within its domain of applicability. However, it has not been tested in environments in which the magnetic field strengths are very strong and the energy densities very great,

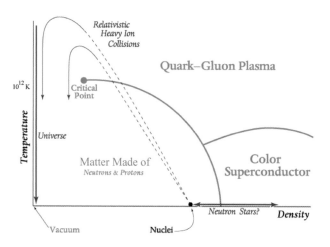

FIGURE 6.4   The phase diagram for quark-based, ordinary matter. At high temperatures or density, a transition from nuclear matter to a plasma of quarks and gluons takes place. Quark-gluon plasmas can be produced at high temperature and low density (early universe), at low temperature and high density (neutron stars), or at moderate temperature and density (at the RHIC facility). The three different methods of producing quark-gluon plasma probe different aspects of the transition. Image courtesy of K. Rajagopal and M. Stock.

nor have the applicable physical principles in these environments been elucidated. Observing the polarization of x rays from pulsars, magnetars, and perhaps gamma-ray bursts would allow just this.

How Were the Elements from Iron to Uranium Made?

The production of the light elements in the big bang and of the elements up to iron in supernovae is in quantitative agreement with observation. Beyond iron, the general conditions needed to make the elements seem clear, but the locale and means of production are unknown. Supernovae or neutron stars are thought to be likely sites for the origin of the heavy elements. By combining full three-dimensional calculations of supernova explosion in a terascale computation, experimental measurements of neutrino-oscillation physics, experimental data on the r-process and rp-process nuclei far from stability, and x-ray and gamma-ray observations of newly formed elements in supernovae, it may be possible to pin down the source of the heaviest elements.

How Do Cosmic Accelerators Work and What Are They Accelerating?

On both spectral and astrophysical grounds, it seems that ultrahigh-energy protons are formed in extremely powerful yet local sources. Perhaps these sources have already been identified with active galaxies or gamma-ray bursts. Alternatively, a completely new constituent of the universe could be involved, like a topological defect associated with the physics of grand unification. Only by observing many more of these particles, or perhaps the associated gamma rays, neutrinos, and gravitational waves, will scientists be able to distinguish these possibilities. To realize this opportunity, large cosmic-ray air shower detector arrays and observations of high-energy gamma rays and neutrinos will be needed, as described in Box 6.1.

7

Realizing the Opportunities

Based upon the science reviewed in the previous chapters, the committee has identified special opportunities at the intersection of astronomy and physics in the form of eleven key questions that are of deep interest and are ripe for answering.

Some of the critical work needed to address these 11 questions is part of ongoing programs in astronomy and in nuclear, particle, and gravitational physics. Other needed work is spelled out in the most recent astronomy decadal survey[1] or has been recommended by the DOE/NSF High Energy Physics Advisory Panel or their Nuclear Science Advisory Committee.

The committee's recommendations, which are presented at the end of this chapter, are meant to complement and supplement the programs in astronomy and physics already in place or recommended, to ensure that the great opportunities before us are realized. They are in no way intended to override the advice of the groups mentioned above.

In the section entitled "The Eleven Questions," the committee presents the 11 questions and summarizes the type of work needed to answer each of them. The detailed strategy for realizing these scientific opportunities that the committee was charged to develop is laid out in seven recommendations contained in section "Recommendations." The remaining sections provide the justifications for the recommendations and tie the seven recommendations to the science questions.

The committee's seven recommendations do not correspond simply to the questions; the interconnectedness of the science precluded such a mapping. Some of the projects it recommends address more than one science question, while some of the questions have no clear connection to the recommendations, although programs already in place or recommended by

---

[1]National Research Council, *Astronomy and Astrophysics in the New Millennium,* Washington, D.C., National Academy Press, 2001.

other NRC committees or advisory groups will address them. The committee calls for three new initiatives—an experiment to map the polarization of the cosmic microwave background, a wide-field space telescope, and a deep underground laboratory. It adds its support to several other initiatives that were previously put forth or set in place and addresses structural issues.

THE ELEVEN QUESTIONS

What Is Dark Matter?

Dark matter dominates the matter in the universe, but questions remain: How much dark matter is there? Where is it? What is it? Of these, the last is the most fundamental. The questions concerning dark matter can be answered by a combination of astronomical and physical experiments. On small astronomical scales, the quantity and location of dark matter can be studied by utilizing its strong gravitational lensing effects on light from distant bright objects and from the distribution and motions of galaxies and hot gas under its gravitational influence. These can be studied using ground-based and space-based optical and infrared telescopes and space-based x-ray telescopes. On larger scales, optical and infrared wide-field survey telescopes can trace the matter distribution via weak gravitational lensing. (Strong gravitational lensing produces multiple images of the lensed objects, while weak gravitational lensing simply distorts the image of the lensed object; see Figure 5.6.) The distribution of dark matter on large scales can be measured by studying motions of galaxies relative to the cosmic expansion. While these observations will measure the quantity and location of dark matter, the ultimate determination of its nature will almost certainly depend on the direct detection of dark matter particles. Ongoing experiments to detect dark matter particles in our Milky Way such as Cold Dark Matter Search II and the US Axion Experiment, future dark-matter experiments in underground laboratories, and accelerator searches for supersymmetric particles at the Fermilab Tevatron or the CERN LHC are all critical. Elements of the program live in the purview of each of three funding agencies, DOE, NASA, and NSF; coordination will be needed to ensure the most effective overall program.

What Is the Nature of the Dark Energy?

There is strong evidence from the study of high-redshift supernovae that the expansion of the universe is accelerating. Fluctuations in the temperature of the CMB indicate that the universe is flat, but the amount of matter is insufficient (by about a factor of 3) to be in accord with this. All this points to the presence of a significant dark energy component, perhaps in the form of a cosmological constant, both to make up the deficit and, through its repulsive gravitational effects, to cause a universal acceleration. This mysterious energy form controls the destiny of the universe and could shed light on the quantum nature of gravity. Because of its diffuse nature, the best methods to probe its properties rely upon its effect on the expansion rate of the universe and the growth of structure in the universe. The use of high-redshift ($z \sim 0.5$ to 1.8) supernovae as cosmic mileposts led to the discovery of cosmic speed up. They have great promise for shedding light on the nature of the dark energy. To do so will require a new class of wide-field telescopes to discover and follow up thousands of supernovae as well as a better understanding of type Ia supernovae to establish that they really are standard candles. In addition, clusters of galaxies can be detected out to redshifts as large as 2 or 3 through x-ray surveys, through large-area radio and millimeter-wave surveys using the Sunyaev-Zel'dovich effect and through gravitational lensing. Future x-ray missions will be able to determine the redshifts and masses of these clusters. High-redshift supernovae, counts of galaxy clusters, weak-gravitational lensing, and the microwave background all provide complementary information about the existence and properties of dark energy. Already NASA and NSF have programs and special expertise in parts of this science with their traditional roles in space- and ground-based astronomy, while DOE has made contributions in areas such as CCD detector development. Again, interagency cooperation and coordination will be needed to define and manage this research optimally.

How Did the Universe Begin?

The inflationary paradigm, that the very early universe underwent a very large and rapid expansion, is now supported by observations of tiny fluctuations in the intensity of the CMB. The exact cause of inflation is still unknown. Inflation leaves a telltale signature of gravitational waves, which can be used to test the theory and distinguish between different models of inflation. Direct detection of the gravitational radiation from inflation might be possible in the future with very-long-baseline, space-based laser interferometer gravitational-wave detectors. A promising shorter-term approach is to search for the signature of these gravitational waves in the polarized radiation from the CMB. If the relevant polarization signals are strong enough, they may be detected by the current generation of balloon-borne and satellite experiments, such as MAP, which is now taking data, and the European Planck satellite, planned for launch late in this decade. However, it is likely that a more sensitive satellite mission devoted to polarization measurements will be required. Support for detector development is critical to realizing such a mission. NSF, NASA, and DOE have already played important roles in CMB science, and their cooperation in the future will be essential.

Did Einstein Have the Last Word on Gravity?

Although general relativity has been tested over a range of length scales and physical conditions, it has not been tested in the extreme conditions near black holes. Its predicted gravitational waves have been indirectly observed, but not directly detected and studied in detail. Gravity has not been unified with the other forces, nor has Einstein's theory been generalized to include quantum effects. A host of experiments are now probing possible effects arising from the unification of general relativity with other forces, from laboratory-scale precision experiments to test the principle of equivalence and the force law of gravity to the search for the production of black holes at accelerators. Space experiments envisioned in NASA's Beyond Einstein plan will further test general relativity. Constellation-X, a high-resolution x-ray spectroscopic mission, will be able to probe the regions near the event horizons of black holes by measuring the red- and blueshifts of spectral lines emitted by gas accreting onto the black holes. LISA, a space-based laser interferometer gravitational-wave observatory, will be able to probe the space-time around black holes by detecting the gravitational radiation from merging massive black holes. DOE, NASA, and NSF all have roles to play in establishing a better understanding of gravity.

What Are the Masses of the Neutrinos and How Have They Shaped the Evolution of the Universe?

The discovery that neutrinos have mass and can oscillate among their different types has implications for both the universe and the laws that govern it. Further progress in understanding the masses and oscillations of neutrinos will require an ongoing program of large-scale detectors to study neutrinos from atmospheric and solar sources, striving eventually for sensitivity to the low-energy neutrinos from the proton-proton sequence of nuclear reactions. Experiments that send beams of neutrinos from accelerators to remote detectors (e.g., MINOS) will also provide critical information on neutrino masses and mixing. Detectors will need to be stable and to run for extended periods if they are to provide a window for the observation and timing of neutrinos from any nearby supernova event. Finally, the absolute scale of neutrino masses can be probed by end-point studies of beta decay and high-sensitivity searches for neutrinoless double beta decay. If neutrino masses are large enough, they may play a small but detectable role in the development of large-scale structure in the universe. Elements of this program will require a deep underground laboratory. Such an underground laboratory would perform experiments at the intersection of particle and nuclear physics. It is likely that scientists supported by both DOE and NSF will be involved in its programs.

How Do Cosmic Accelerators Work and What Are They Accelerating?

Cosmic rays and photons with energies far in excess of anything we can produce in laboratories have been detected. We do not yet know the sources of these particles and thus cannot understand their production mechanism. Neutrinos may also be produced in association with them. Identifying the sources of ultrahigh-energy cosmic rays requires several kinds of large-scale experiments to collect sufficiently large data samples and determine the particle directions and energies precisely. Dedicated neutrino telescopes of cubic kilometer size in deep water or ice can be used to search for cosmic sources of high-energy neutrinos. Further study of the sources of high-energy gamma-ray bursts will also be relevant. DOE, NASA, and NSF are all involved in studying the highest-energy cosmic particles.

To understand the acceleration mechanisms of these particles, a better understanding of relativistic plasmas is needed. Laboratory experiments that use high-energy-density pulses to probe relativistic plasma effects can provide important tests of our ability to model the phenomena in astrophysical environments that are the likely sources of intense high-energy particles and radiation. Laboratory work thus will help to guide the development of a theory of cosmic accelerators, as well as to refine our understanding of other astrophysical phenomena that involve relativistic plasmas. This work will require significant interagency and interdisciplinary coordination. The facilities that can produce intense high-energy pulses in plasmas are laser or accelerator facilities funded by DOE. The expertise needed to bring these resources to bear on astrophysical phenomena crosses both disciplinary and agency boundaries.

Are Protons Unstable?

The observed preponderance of matter over antimatter in the universe may be tied to interactions that change baryon number and that violate matter-antimatter (CP) symmetry. Further, baryon number violation is a signature of theories that unify the forces and particles of nature. Two possible directions to search for baryon-number-changing interactions are direct searches for proton decay and searches for evidence of neutron-antineutron oscillations. To attack proton decay at an order of magnitude increase in sensitivity over current limits will require a large detector in a deep underground location. It will also be desirable to achieve improved sensitivity to decay modes involving a kaon and a neutrino, as well as to modes involving a pion and a positron. These searches are complemented by the program in CP violation physics involving kaon and B-meson decays, which is a central part of the ongoing high-energy physics agenda. In the future, it may be feasible to determine CP violation in neutrino interactions in an underground lab via long-baseline experiments with intense neutrino beams from accelerators. As in the case of the related neutrino experiments mentioned above, this work will require coordinated planning among all agencies supporting any underground laboratory.

What Are the New States of Matter at Exceedingly High Density and Temperature?

Computer simulations of quantum chromodynamics (QCD) have provided evidence that at high temperature and density, matter undergoes a transition to a state known as the quark-gluon plasma. The existence and properties of this new phase of matter have important cosmological implications. Quark-gluon plasmas may also play a role in the interiors of neutron stars. Some, but not all, aspects of the transition from ordinary matter to a quark-gluon plasma can be probed with accelerators (see Figure 6.4). Experiments at the Relativistic Heavy-Ion Collider (RHIC) at Brookhaven National Laboratory may probe the transition to a quark-gluon plasma in the fireball formed when two massive nuclei collide at high energy. If this phase existed in the early universe, it may have left its signature in a gravitational-wave signal. The LISA space gravitational-wave interferometer will begin a search for this signal, but a follow-on experiment with higher sensitivity may be needed in order to observe it. Transitions to other new phases of matter may have occurred in the early universe and left detectable gravitational-wave signatures (possibilities include transitions to states where the forces of nature are unified). X-ray observations of neutron stars can shed light on how matter behaves at nuclear and higher densities, providing insights about the physics of nuclear matter and possibly even of new states of matter.

Are There Additional Space-Time Dimensions?

Theories containing more than four dimensions (with at least some of the additional dimensions having macroscopic scale) have been suggested as the explanation for why the observed gravitational force is so small compared with the other fundamental forces. Such theories have two types of possible experimental signature. Small-scale precision experiments can search for deviations from standard predictions for the strength of gravity on the submillimeter scale. High-energy accelerator searches can test for events with missing energy, signaling the production of gravitons, evidence for the excitations of a compact additional dimension. Accelerator searches for new particles and/or missing energy are typically not done with a dedicated experiment but by additional analyses of data collected in high-energy collision experiments. It is important for the agencies to recognize the value of these analyses, even if they do not find the desired effect but instead set new limits. This science falls into the realms of both NSF and DOE.

How Were the Elements from Iron to Uranium Made?

While we have a relatively complete understanding of the origin of elements lighter than iron, important details in the production of elements from iron to uranium remain a puzzle. A sequence of rapid neutron captures by nuclei, known as the r-process, is clearly involved, as may be seen from the observed abundances of the various elements. Supernova explosions, neutron-star mergers, or gamma-ray bursters are possible locales for this process, but our incomplete understanding of these events leaves the question open. Progress requires work on a number of fronts. More realistic simulations of supernova explosions and neutron star mergers are essential; they will require access to large-scale computing facilities. In addition, better measurements are needed for both the inputs and the outputs of these calculations.

The masses and other properties of neutrinos are crucial parts of the input. The masses and lifetimes of many nuclei that cannot be reached with existing technology are also important input parameters; however, a complete theoretical description of such nuclei remains out of reach. Almost all the relevant r-process nuclei could be accessible for study in a suitably designed two-stage acceleration facility (such as RIA) that produces isotopes and reaccelerates them. Such a facility has been recommended by NSAC as a high-priority project for nuclear physics.

For the outputs, sensitive high-energy x-ray and gamma-ray space experiments will allow us to observe the decays of newly formed elements soon after supernova explosions and other major astrophysical events. Comparison of these observations with the outputs of simulations can constrain the theoretical models for the explosions. Better measurements of abundances of certain heavy elements in cosmic rays may also provide useful constraints.

The program suggested above spans nuclear physics, astrophysics, and particle physics and will require coordination between all three agencies.

Is a New Theory of Matter and Light Needed at the Highest Energies?

While few scientists expect that the theory of QED will fail in any astrophysical environment, checking the consistency of observations with predictions of this theory does provide a way to test the self-consistency of astrophysical models and mechanisms. The predictions of QED have been tested with great precision in regimes accessible to laboratory study, such as in static magnetic fields as large as roughly 10^5 gauss. However, magnetic fields as large as 10^{12} gauss are commonly found on the surfaces of neutron stars (pulsars), and a subset of neutron stars, called magnetars, have magnetic field strengths in the range 10^{14} to 10^{15} gauss, well above the QED critical field, where quantum effects produce polarized radiation. As magnetars rotate rather slowly, it may be possible to observe this polarization and map out the neutron star magnetic field. To carry out such observations will require x-ray instruments capable of measuring polarization.

―――――――――

As can be seen from these brief summaries, important parts of the answers to the 11 questions lie squarely in the central plans of the core disciplines of high-energy physics, nuclear physics, plasma physics, or astrophysics, and much exciting science relevant to our questions is already being pursued. The fact that the recommendations made in this report do not speak directly to existing programs should not be construed as lack of support for those programs. Rather the committee has been charged to focus attention on projects or programs that because they lie between the traditional disciplines may have fallen through the cracks. When viewed from the broader perspective this science takes on a greater urgency and must be made a priority.

It is also notable that many of the efforts described above have features that fall within the purview of more than one agency, or involve competing approaches that, in the present system, would be reviewed by different agencies. To ensure that the approach to these problems follows the most effective path, interagency cooperation is needed, not just at the stage of funding decisions but also at the level of project oversight when a project is funded through more than one agency.

UNDERSTANDING THE BIRTH OF THE UNIVERSE

The CMB is a relic from a very early time in the history of the universe. The spectrum and anisotropy of the CMB have already given us valuable information about the birth of the universe and provide some evidence that the universe went through an inflationary epoch. Future measurements of the polarization of the anisotropy of the CMB are the most promising way to definitively test inflation and to learn directly about the inflationary epoch.

The photons of the CMB come to us from a time when their creation and destruction effectively stopped because the universe had expanded to relatively low densities. The spectrum of the CMB differs from that of a blackbody by less than 1 part in 10^4, showing that the energy of CMB photons has not been perturbed since about 2 months after the big bang. For the next 400,000 years, photon-electron scattering scrambled only the directions of the photons. When the universe cooled to about 3000 K, electrons and baryons combined to form neutral atoms. After this "recombination" or last-scattering epoch, the CMB photons traveled freely across the universe, allowing us to compare those coming from parts of the universe that are very distant from us with those coming from parts nearby. In this way the anisotropy of the CMB can reveal the distribution of matter in the universe as it was a half million years after the big bang, before the creation of stars and galaxies.

Efforts to detect the anisotropy of the CMB started immediately after its discovery. Initially, only the anisotropy due to the motion of the solar system at 370 km/sec relative to the average velocity of the observable universe was found. Finally, in 1992, the Differential Microwave Radiometer (DMR) instrument on the Cosmic Background Explorer (COBE) satellite detected the intrinsic anisotropy of the CMB at a level of 10 parts per million.

The DMR detected these 30 millionths of a degree temperature differences across the sky by integrating for a full year. The DMR beam size (about 7 degrees), when projected to the edge of the observable universe, spans a region a few times larger than the distance light could have traveled in the half million years between the big bang and the last scattering. As a result, the anisotropy seen by the DMR is truly primordial, unaffected by the interaction between the CMB and matter. But interactions between the CMB and matter are a critical part of the later formation of clusters and superclusters of galaxies, and these interactions can be studied by looking at the CMB with smaller beam sizes. These interactions produce a series of "acoustic" peaks in the plot of temperature difference vs. angular scale, with scales of a degree and smaller (see Figure 5.3). They are called acoustic because they record the effect of the interaction of the radiation with matter variations analogous to sound waves.

When looking at small angular scales, the foreground interference from the atmosphere is less of a problem, and experiments on the ground and on stratospheric balloons have observed evidence for a series of acoustic peaks. These experiments have shown by the position of the first peak that the geometry of our universe is consistent with being uncurved, and by the height of the second peak have made an independent measurement of the amount of ordinary matter in the universe. The existence of acoustic peaks and the flatness of the geometry of the universe are consistent with the predictions of inflation and have given the theory its first significant tests. The determination of the amount of ordinary matter, about 4 percent of the critical density, agrees with the determination based on the amount of deuterium produced during the first seconds and strengthens the case for a new form of dark matter dominating the mass in the universe.

For the future, the Microwave Anisotropy Probe (MAP), launched on June 30, 2001, will measure the entire sky with a 0.2-degree beam and a sensitivity 45 times better than that of the DMR. The European Space Agency's Planck satellite, to be launched in 2007, will have a 0.08-degree beam and a sensitivity 20 times better than MAP. Since anisotropy signals on even smaller angular scales are suppressed by the finite thickness of the surface of last scattering, MAP and Planck will essentially complete the study of the temperature differences resulting from these primordial density fluctuations. We expect to learn much about the earliest moments of the universe from these two very important missions.

There remains one critical feature of the microwave sky to be explored: its polarization. Polarization promises to reveal unique features of the early universe, but it will be difficult to measure. First, its anisotropies are expected to be an order of magnitude smaller than those for the temperature field. This means that more sensitive detectors and longer integration times are required.

And second, it is likely that polarizing galactic foregrounds will be more troublesome than they are for determining the temperature field.

At every point on the sky, the temperature of the radiation can be represented as a single number, while polarization is represented by a line segment (see Figure 4.6). For example, a given point may have a temperature of 2.725 degrees and its temperature may differ from the average by 30 millionths of a degree. But the signal measured by a polarized detector aligned toward the north galactic pole might exceed that measured by a detector aligned in the east-west direction by just two millionths of a degree. The polarization line segment in this example would point north-south, and its length would be related to the latter temperature difference. The science comes from a study of the pattern of these line segments on the sky and how they correlate with the temperature pattern. To reveal this polarization field, more sensitive detectors with polarization sensitivity are required.

According to our understanding of the oscillations in the plasma of photons, electrons, and baryons that were under way before recombination, the inhomogeneities that developed lead naturally to a predictable level of polarization of the CMB photons. This polarization anisotropy is expected to be most prominent at even finer angular scales than those for the temperature, requiring instruments with beams that are smaller than 0.1 degrees.

In the fall of 2002, the first detection of the polarization of the anisotropy of the CMB by the DASI experiment was announced (see Figure 4.6); the amplitude and variation with angular scale was as expected. Nearly two dozen efforts are under way to further characterize the polarization. While most are modifications of existing temperature anisotropy experiments, some are dedicated to detecting polarization. These ongoing efforts are also important in that they will allow accurate study of the foregrounds that are expected to contaminate the measurements.

It is highly likely that experiments already in progress will systematically characterize the CMB polarization and the associated foregrounds. This will be an important confirmation of our understanding of the initial fluctuations that led to anisotropies and structure formation. However, these experiments (including MAP and Planck, which have polarization sensitivity) will not be able to fully characterize the polarization of the CMB anisotropy because their sensitivity is not adequate. Measuring CMB polarization in essence triples the information we can obtain about the earliest moments and exploits the full information available from this most important relic of the early universe.

The most important long-range goal of polarization studies is to detect the consequences of gravitational waves produced during the inflationary epoch. The existence of these gravitational waves is the third key prediction of inflation (after flatness and the existence of acoustic peaks). Moreover, the strength of the gravitational wave signal is a direct indicator of when inflation took place, which would help to unravel the mystery of what caused inflation.

The gravitational waves arising from inflation correspond to a distortion in the fabric of space-time and imprint a distinctive pattern on the polarization of the CMB that cannot be mimicked by that from density fluctuations. This so-called "B-mode" component of the polarization will have amplitudes one or more orders of magnitude smaller than the polarization produced by normal scattering between the photons and matter. This gravity wave signal occurs on relatively large angular scales, greater than about 2 degrees, which is the scale of the observable universe at recombination. Very large sky coverage, high sensitivity, and excellent control of systematic errors are necessary to measure this submicrokelvin signal.

Based on what is known about polarization foregrounds and the existence of a false B-mode signal produced by gravitational lensing, a fully optimized experiment might well be able to detect gravitational waves from inflation, even if their effect on the CMB is three orders of magnitude smaller than that of density perturbations. Achieving this sensitivity would allow one to probe inflation models whose energy scale is 3×10^{15} GeV or larger, close to the energy where the forces are expected to be unified.

While there is no question about the great scientific importance of detecting the B-mode signature of inflation, it must be pointed out that the challenges to doing so are just as great. Still unknown foregrounds or contaminants could preclude achieving the proposed sensitivity, and even if the proposed sensitivity is achieved, the signal, while present, could go undetected because it is too small.

To achieve this extremely ambitious goal, significant detector R&D is needed over 3 or 4 years. The most promising detectors appear to be large-format bolometer arrays, the challenge being to read out signals from compact arrays of several thousand detectors. It is important that this R&D effort be supported and that parallel efforts be encouraged. Ground-based and balloon-borne observations will provide experience with different detection schemes (particularly on how to guard against false polarization signals) and will provide more information about galactic foregrounds. A coordinated program of laboratory research, ground-based and balloon-borne observations, and finally a space mission dedicated to CMB polarization will be required to get the very best sensitivity to this important signature (and probe) of inflation. Planning for a space mission should begin now, but the final detector design must depend on experience gained through the R&D effort.

The committee notes that it was a broad and coordinated approach that made possible the current successes in learning about the early universe from the anisotropy of the CMB. DOE, NASA, and NSF have all played roles in the anisotropy success story, and all three have roles to play in the quest to detect the polarization signal of inflation.

UNDERSTANDING THE DESTINY OF THE UNIVERSE

Of the 11 questions that the committee has posed, the nature of dark energy is probably the most vexing. It has been called the deepest mystery in physics, and its resolution is likely to greatly advance our understanding of matter, space, and time.

The simplest and most direct observational argument for the presence of dark energy comes from type Ia supernovae at high redshift. In our immediate neighborhood, with proper corrections applied, the intrinsic luminosities of such supernovae are seen to be remarkably uniform, making them useful as "standard candles" for cosmological measurements. Using Type Ia supernovae as cosmic mileposts to probe the expansion history of the universe leads to the remarkable conclusion that the expansion is speeding up instead of slowing down, as would be expected from the gravitational pull of its material content. This implies that the energy content of the universe is dominated by a mysterious dark energy whose gravity is repulsive.

A spatially flat universe (like ours) containing matter only would continue to expand and slow indefinitely. The existence of dark energy changes all that. Depending upon the nature of the dark energy, the universe could continue its speed-up, begin slowing, or even recollapse. If this cosmic speed-up continues, the sky will become essentially devoid of visible galaxies in only 150 billion years. Until we understand dark energy, we cannot understand the destiny of the universe.

We have few clues about the physics of the dark energy. It could be as "simple" as the energy associated with nature's quantum vacuum. Or, it is possible that our current description of a universe with dark matter and dark energy may just be a clumsy construction of epicycles that we are patching together to save what could be an obsolete theoretical framework. Also puzzling is the fact that we seem to be living at a special time in cosmic history, when the dark energy appears only recently to have begun to dominate over dark and other forms of matter.

The supernova data become more compelling with each new observation. We have no evidence so far, for example, that "gray dust" is obscuring supernovae at high redshift nor that the supernovae are evolving, two effects that could weaken their credibility as standard candles. Recent observations of very high redshift objects such as SN 1997ff support this conclusion. Moreover, the supernova observations are fully compatible with other cosmological observations. We know from the CMB that the universe is spatially flat and therefore that its total matter and energy density must sum to the critical density. On the other hand, all our measurements of the amount of normal and dark matter indicate that matter accounts for only one third of the critical energy density. The dark energy neatly accounts for the remaining two thirds.

We have a significant chance over the next two decades to discern the properties of the dark energy. Because this mysterious new substance is so diffuse, the cosmos is the primary site where it can be studied. The gravitational effects of dark energy are determined by the ratio of its pressure to its energy density. The more negative its pressure, the more repulsive the gravity of the dark energy. The dark energy influences the expansion rate of the universe, in turn governing the rate at which structure grows and the correlation between redshift and distance.

The means of probing the cosmological effects of dark energy include the measurement of the apparent luminosity of Type Ia supernovae as a function of redshift, the study of the number density of galaxies and clusters of galaxies as a function of redshift, and the use of weak gravitational lensing to study the growth of structure in the universe. Given the fundamental nature of this endeavor, it is essential to approach it with a variety of methods requiring not only the full array of existing instruments but also a new class of telescopes on the ground and in space. Many of these measurements can also provide important information on the amount and distribution of dark matter.

In the near term, the search for high-redshift Type Ia supernovae will rely on wide-field cameras on 4-meter-class telescopes. Follow-up observations of the supernovae light curves will use the Hubble Space Telescope (when possible), while spectroscopic measurements that test for possible evolutionary effects are obtained with 8- to 10-meter telescopes. Further evidence for cosmic speed-up and some information about the equation of state of the dark energy can be expected.

The study of the growth of structure and the measurement of the number density of galaxies and clusters will have to combine several methods. One of these is a program of galaxy surveys in the visible and near infrared at low redshift (such as the Sloan Digital Sky Survey and the 2MASS) and at high redshift (such as the DEEP Survey). Characterization of the hot plasmas present in clusters by x-ray satellites such as Chandra and XMM-Newton will also be important. Mapping of the distortions of the cosmic microwave background caused by hot cluster gas (Sunyaev-Zel'dovich effect) will be used to find and count clusters as well as to understand their evolution. New instruments, especially Constellation-X, which is planned for the end of the decade, should lead to further progress in the study of galaxy clusters.

Pilot studies of the gravitational distortion of the images of distant galaxies by intervening mass concentrations (weak gravitational lensing) show the power of this method for measuring the evolution of structure and for identifying and determining the masses of galaxy clusters. This method will soon be more fully exploited as new large CCD cameras become fully operational on large telescopes.

All these observations depend upon the development of advanced photon sensors in the optical, millimeter, infrared, and x-ray portions of the spectrum and upon the training of instrumentalists who can integrate these sensors into new instruments. Moreover, the whole enterprise must be linked to a vigorous theory and computational program that explores not only the fundamental nature and origin of dark energy but also the phenomenology of the complex astronomical objects that we use as probes (e.g., supernovae, galaxies, and clusters).

In spite of its importance, the program discussed above will only be able to chip away at the problem of dark energy. To understand its properties fully we will need a new class of optical and near-infrared telescopes with very large fields of view (greater than one square degree) and gigapixel cameras. They will be needed to measure much larger numbers of supernovae with control of systematics and to map gravitational lensing over large scales. There is a need for one such telescope on the ground—such as the Large Synoptic Survey Telescope (LSST), recommended by the Astronomy and Astrophysics Survey Committee[2]—and one in space—such as the proposed SuperNova Acceleration Probe (SNAP).

A 6- to 8-meter wide-field telescope on the ground will be able to carry out weak gravitational lensing maps of over 10,000 square degrees with individual exposures on the order of 7 square degrees. From these observations, tens of thousands of galaxy clusters can be discovered and their masses determined, and the development of structure can be probed. A

---

[2]National Research Council, *Astronomy and Astrophysics in the New Millennium,* Washington, D.C., National Academy Press, 2001.

wide-field, ground-based telescope will also be very effective in monitoring the sky for variable events, from near-Earth objects to transient astrophysical phenomena such as gamma-ray bursts and supernovae. Such a telescope will discover large numbers of moderate redshift supernovae and measure their light curves. The ability of LSST to explore the astronomical "time domain" was the main reason the survey committee recommended it as a high-priority project.

A wide-field space telescope would probably be much smaller in aperture (2-meter diameter for SNAP) and field of view (around 1 square degree) because of weight and cost considerations, but it would benefit significantly from being above Earth's atmosphere. A wide-field space telescope could discover thousands of distant Type Ia supernovae and follow their light curves in the optical and near-infrared. Operating above the atmosphere ensures uniform sampling of light curves without regard to weather and helps to minimize systematic errors or corrections. Spectroscopic follow-up of each supernova by a wide-field space telescope (if it has such a capability) or by other telescopes is essential to study potential systematics, including evolution. A wide-field space telescope could, over a few years, put together a high-quality, very uniform sample of several thousand supernovae. Using this sample, the equation of state of dark energy could be determined to about 5 percent and tested for variation with time.

A wide-field space telescope is also well suited for deep, weak-gravitational lensing studies of the evolution of structure over small areas of sky to probe dark energy. The absence of atmospheric distortion allows fainter, more distant, smaller galaxies to be used for this purpose. Finally, a wide-field space telescope will have other astronomical capabilities, e.g., providing targets for the Next Generation Space Telescope (NGST) and searching for transient astronomical phenomena.

Why two wide-field telescopes? The range of redshifts where the dark energy can be studied in detail is from $z \sim 0.2$ to $z \sim 2$ (at higher redshifts, the dark energy becomes too small a fraction of the total energy density to study effectively, and at small redshifts the observables are insensitive to the composition of the universe). Our almost complete ignorance of the nature of dark energy and its importance argues for probing it as completely as possible. To do this, two complementary capabilities are needed: (1) the ability to observe to redshifts as large as 2 with high resolution and in the rest frame visible band and (2) the ability to cover large portions of the sky to redshifts as large as unity. The combination of ground- and space-based wide-field telescopes will do just that. Space offers high resolution and access to the near-infrared (which for objects at redshifts as high as 2 corresponds to the rest frame visible band). The ground enables the large aperture (8-meter class) needed to quickly cover large portions of the sky.

A wide-field space telescope can discover and follow up thousands of type Ia supernovae, the simplest and most direct probes of the expansion, to study the effect of dark energy on the expansion out to redshifts $z \sim 2$. This is because the light from these most distant objects is shifted to near-infrared wavelengths, which must be studied from space. Space observations also minimize the systematic errors by providing the high resolution needed to separate the supernova light from that of the host galaxy and by guaranteeing that the entire light curve is observed, since atmospheric weather is not a problem. While a space-based wide-field telescope is first a high-precision, distant supernova detector, it can also extend the weak-gravitational lensing technique to the highest redshifts because it has sufficient resolution to measure the shapes of the most distant galaxies.

A ground-based wide-field telescope has its greatest power in studying the dark energy at redshifts of less than about 1. It can discover tens of thousands of supernovae out to redshifts of about $z \sim 0.8$ and follow them up (though not with the same control of systematics that can be done in space). It can carry out weak-gravitational-lensing surveys over thousands of square degrees to moderate depth. Such surveys can probe the dark energy by measuring its effect on the development of large-scale structure and by measuring the evolution of the abundance of clusters (the latter work extends and complements x-ray and Sunyaev-Zel'dovich effect measurements that will be made).

EXPLORING THE UNIFICATION OF THE FORCES FROM UNDERGROUND

Between the 1896 discovery of radioactivity and the development of particle accelerators, the cosmic rays constantly bombarding Earth were essential tools for scientific progress in particle physics. Among the successes were the discoveries of the anti-electron (positron), the pi meson (pion), and the mu meson (muon). However, when it comes to addressing three of the questions—What is dark matter? What are the masses of the neutrinos? Is the proton stable?—the cosmic rays that were once the signal have now become the source of a limiting background.

With the known exception of neutrinos, which penetrate everything, most cosmic rays are readily absorbed in the atmosphere and in Earth's surface. However, muons are absorbed only slowly as they pass through matter. The most penetrating muons, which can produce other radioactive particles, can be removed only by locating the experiment under a substantial overburden (see Figure 7.1). Scientists have sought ever deeper underground environments, well shielded from cosmic-ray muons, to carry out the forefront experiments that address our questions.

The earliest ideas for a water detector capable of detecting the decay of protons and the interactions of neutrinos from the Sun and other cosmic sources trace to the late 1970s in the United States. Though some pioneering underground experiments were done here in the early 1980s, Japan

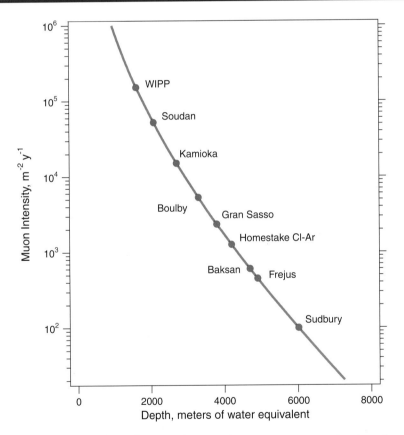

FIGURE 7.1   The number of penetrating cosmic-ray muons vs. overburden of earth (measured in mwe—meters of water equivalent; 1 mwe is approximately 1 foot of material). Existing underground labs are WIPP, Homestake, and Soudan in the United States; Kamioka in Japan; Boulby, Gran Sasso, Baksan, and Frejus in Europe; and Sudbury in Canada. There is a deeper option in the Homestake mine at about the same depth as Sudbury. Figure courtesy of R.G.H. Robertson.

created a major research program in this new area at the Kamioka mine. In 1998, data from Super-Kamiokande, at a depth of about 3,000 meters of water equivalent (mwe), provided convincing evidence that muon neutrinos mix, or oscillate, with electron or tau neutrinos. This can occur only if neutrinos have mass.

About 30 years ago, U.S. investigators found the first indications of oscillations in electron-family solar neutrinos at the Homestake mine (located near the level of the existing chlorine-argon experiment). Since then, other experiments in Europe and Asia have seen similar manifestations of electron-neutrino oscillations. The Sudbury Neutrino Observatory (SNO) in Canada unambiguously demonstrated the oscillation of solar electron neutrinos, but required a depth of 6,000 mwe to achieve sufficiently low cosmic-ray backgrounds. The establishment of appropriate infrastructure to assemble and operate SNO at this depth accounted for a substantial part of the cost and the construction time.

The Laboratori Nazionali del Gran Sasso, in Italy, and a facility in the Baksan valley in Russia are two general-purpose national underground laboratory facilities (see Figure 7.1). With substantial infrastructure and good access, Gran Sasso (3,400 mwe) represents the kind of facility required to make progress in this field. However, Gran Sasso and Baksan have limited remaining experimental space and insufficient depth for some experiments at the cutting edge today.

There is now good evidence that neutrinos have mass, a phenomenon that points to a grander framework for the particles and forces, since neutrino mass cannot be accommodated within the Standard Model. However, the quantitative parameters associated with neutrino mass and mixing have not yet been accurately measured. Experiments studying oscillations of neutrinos aim to establish clearly the extent of neutrino family mixing, the relationships among the masses for the physical neutrino states, and particle-antiparticle asymmetries. This is a compelling scientific objective that bears not only on the unification of the forces but also on the formation of large-scale structure in the universe and on the production of the chemical elements in supernova explosions.

The richness of the information requires many approaches. Some data will be obtained using neutrinos made on Earth at reactors and at accelerators. However, to measure neutrino oscillations, the target detectors need to be located at substantial distance from the sources. Other experiments can utilize neutrinos created in the Sun and the atmosphere. To exploit these natural sources of neutrinos, low ambient backgrounds and detection of the very low-energy solar neutrinos are essential. Appropriate underground facilities are essential to do either; one facility could conceivably do both. Many techniques are being studied to carry out these experiments, and most require substantial depth, in some cases at least 4,000 mwe.

Careful study of the end point of the beta decay of tritium has allowed setting a neutrino mass limit of a few electron-volts; experiments in progress might be able to probe as low as a few tenths of an electron-volt. The search for neutrinoless double beta decay can reveal if neutrinos are their own antiparticles, and can yield information about neutrino masses. Such experiments now probe neutrino masses as small as a few tenths of an electron-volt; proposed experiments might be able to probe neutrino masses as small as 0.01 eV. Reaching this level is important as it includes the smallest mass consistent with that implied by the atmospheric neutrino experiments. Like oscillation experiments, double beta decay experiments require extraordinarily low backgrounds and hence great depths. Massive neutrinos may even play a role in the origin of the matter-antimatter critical to the existence of ordinary matter in the universe.

Massive neutrinos contribute about as much to the universe's matter budget as do stars, but they are unlikely to constitute the bulk of the dark matter. The lightest supersymmetric particle (neutralino) or the axion are more plausible candidates. Identifying the dark matter particle is a high priority. Neutralinos could be produced and discovered with accelerators, but their production may be beyond the capabilities of existing and planned accelerators. It is therefore essential to seek evidence for neutralinos in direct searches. Experiments in the United States are operating and actively seeking to detect the neutralinos or axions that make up the dark matter in our own galaxy. No compelling signal has been found yet. More sensitive (second-generation) experiments, currently being assembled, will soon significantly increase our reach.

New techniques for neutralino searches under development show promise. These include high-purity germanium detectors, very massive liquid xenon detectors, and scaling up of the current cryogenic detector techniques. To extend sensitivity, potential techniques include very large low-pressure drift chambers, phonon asymmetry in isotopically pure crystals, or detection of the mechanical recoils. All these new possibilities are exciting but extremely challenging, and they will require sustained development.

Future neutralino searches will likely require greater depth. The irreducible background in such experiments is that of high-energy neutrons (produced by penetrating muons), which cause nuclear recoils in the detector that appear identical to the neutralino scattering. Such a neutron background is already close to being a limiting factor in second-generation experiments at depths of 2,000 mwe. Neutralino search experiments will also benefit from common infrastructure at such a laboratory. Specific examples include a monitoring facility for the radioactive background, availability of materials stored underground for long times so the cosmic ray activation has gone, underground material purification and detector fabrication facilities, and shielded clean rooms with radon scrubbing for assembly of radioactivity-sensitive detector elements.

As far as we know, the proton is completely stable. However, there are reasons to believe that the proton is merely long lived: Nonconservation of baryon number is needed to explain the existence of matter in the universe, and extensions of the Standard Model that unify the forces and particles predict that baryon number is not conserved and predict the recently discovered neutrino oscillations. The observation of proton decay would be evidence for a grander theory of the elementary particles and would help to explain the very existence of matter as well as its ultimate demise. The most sensitive experiment, Super-Kamiokande, placed the best limit on the decay to pion and positron, 1.6×10^{33} years. Proton decay to neutrino and kaon, a mode preferred by supersymmetric theories, is more poorly constrained, because of higher backgrounds and lower efficiencies.

A proposal exists to extend the range of accessible proton lifetimes by a factor of about 10 by using the Super-Kamiokande technique and a larger mass detector. Techniques are also being studied that would provide improved efficiency and smaller backgrounds for the kaon decay mode. Though proton decay experiments typically require only modest depth, the envisaged large detector masses dictate substantial infrastructure, including some of the capabilities described above. Because a proton decay experiment does not necessarily need the greatest depth, the optimal site for such an experiment might be somewhere other than a deep underground laboratory.

An underground facility would provide capabilities to do more than address the scientific issues discussed above. For example, neutrinos created in supernovae could be observed directly. To date, neutrinos from a single supernova in 1987 have been seen. Observation of neutrinos from other supernovae could shed light on the nature of neutrinos, on the origin of the elements beyond the iron group, and on the characteristics of the supernova mechanism.

In many cases, with present knowledge and available technologies, our questions on dark matter, neutrino mass, and proton stability are ripe for major experimental breakthroughs. Such experiments must be in locations well isolated from cosmic rays. To be at the cutting edge, they will be large, expensive, and technically challenging, requiring substantial infrastructure.

Though many experiments require depths of only 4,000 mwe, accommodating future experiments over the next two decades may well require depths up to 6,000 mwe.

To address the questions of neutrino mass, proton stability, and dark matter, there is a compelling need for a facility that will provide both shielding and infrastructure. An underground facility in North America is required if the United States is to play a significant leadership role in the next generation of underground experiments. Several proposals exist to provide a site in North America, including deeper levels at the Homestake mine, a site at San Jacinto, and expansion of the scientific area in the Sudbury mine. With appropriate commitment to infrastructure and experiments, any of these sites could provide the depths required for important future experiments.

EXPLORING THE BASIC LAWS OF PHYSICS FROM SPACE

Employing observations of astronomical objects for testing the laws of physics is not new: The orbits of binary neutron stars and of Mercury around the Sun have been used to test theories of gravity. Astrophysicists are now recognizing that the strong gravitational fields and extreme densities and temperatures found in objects like black holes, neutron stars, and gamma-ray bursts allow us to test established laws of physics in new and unfamiliar regimes.

A key scientific component of NASA's Beyond Einstein initiative is the use of space-based observatories to probe physics in extreme regimes not accessible on Earth. Several missions and development programs directly address a number of the 11 questions considered here. However, the Beyond Einstein initiative is broad and includes elements not directly relevant to the science the committee discusses in this report.

The Beyond Einstein missions relevant for this study include one already under construction (GLAST), two programs (Constellation-X and LISA) undergoing active technology development and detailed mission studies, and a number of advanced concepts and technology programs. Constellation-X and LISA were accorded high priority in the NRC's *Astronomy and Astrophysics in the New Millennium* on the basis of their ability to answer key questions in astronomy. Here, we address their unique capabilities to study gravity, matter, and light in new regimes.

Constellation-X is a high-throughput x-ray observatory emphasizing high spectral resolution and broad band-pass. It utilizes lightweight, large-area x-ray optics and microcalorimeters as well as grating spectrometers to cover an energy range from 0.25 to 10 keV. A coaligned hard x-ray telescope extends spectral coverage to 60 keV. It will improve sensitivity by a factor of 25–100 relative to current high-spectral-resolution x-ray instruments.

Constellation-X will measure the line shapes and time variations of spectral lines, particularly iron K-fluorescence, produced when x rays illuminate dense material accreting onto massive black holes, thus probing the space-time geometry outside the hole to within a few gravitational radii. Current measurements of the broadening of x-ray lines emitted near black holes show variable Doppler shifts and gravitational redshifts, providing evidence that at least a few are spinning. Much more sensitive observations of line shapes with Constellation-X will measure the actual black-hole spin rates. Constellation-X will also measure continuum flares and subsequent changes in line emission, providing data on the effect of gravity on time near a black hole and thereby testing the validity of general relativity in the strong gravity limit.

Additional tests of general relativity can be made by observing quasi-periodic oscillations (QPOs) of the x-ray flux emitted by matter falling onto neutron stars or black holes in galactic binaries. The modulations producing the QPOs almost certainly originate in regions of strong gravity. With its large collecting area, Constellation-X will provide essential new x-ray data, as could future missions specifically designed for high-time-resolution studies of bright sources.

In addition to having strong gravitational fields, collapsed stellar remnants produce densities even higher than in an atomic nucleus. Nuclei are held together by forces involving their constituent quarks and mediated by gluons. What happens at higher densities and temperatures is unknown. Accelerators such as RHIC may be able to generate momentary quark-gluon plasmas with a density 10 times that of nuclei to probe the state(s) of matter at extremely high energy density. Neutron stars (created in supernova explosions) have core densities that are almost certainly much higher than those of nuclei. The core temperature, however, is probably on the order of 10^9 K, or ~1,000 times cooler than that expected for a quark-gluon plasma produced at an accelerator. Thus, neutron stars contain states of nuclear material that cannot be re-created on Earth.

Various models for the behavior of matter under such conditions make specific predictions for the relationship between neutron star mass and radius, as well as for the cooling rates of newly formed neutron stars. Some masses have been determined by measuring orbits of neutron stars in binary systems. Neutron star radii are sometimes inferred by spectral measurements of hot atmospheres formed after thermonuclear explosions (seen as x-ray bursts) on surfaces of accreting neutron stars; however, the inferred values can be systematically wrong if the x rays come from a hot spot on the surface or an extended atmosphere. X-ray continuum measurements have been used to estimate temperatures and radii for a few systems. Observations with Constellation-X can search for spectral lines (and absorption features) in bursting sources, in binary systems, and in isolated neutron star atmospheres. Offsets in the central wavelengths of the spectral features determine the gravitational redshift. Widths and strengths of lines measure rotation speed or pressure broadening near the neutron star surface. Such data can determine neutron star mass and radius and constrain the compressibility of "cold" nuclear matter, thereby providing keys to understanding its underlying composition and particle interactions or equation of state.

Another technique is to use x-ray observations of neutron stars of known ages to determine the cooling rates, which in turn depend on structure and processes in the stellar interior. There are only a handful of supernova remnants in our galaxy with a historically observed and recorded explosion. The Chandra X-ray Observatory is using its superb angular resolution to isolate young neutron stars amid the debris in several of these systems. The highly sensitive Constellation-X spectrometers will then be able to observe stars located by Chandra and determine the surface temperature and shape of the energy spectrum. These data can be compared with cooling models whose detailed predictions are sensitive to the composition and equation of state of the interior.

LISA is a gravitational-wave detector consisting of a triangular formation of three spacecraft separated by 5 million km. Laser beams transmitted between the spacecraft can measure miniscule changes in path length between reflecting "proof masses" located in each satellite. Tiny changes in path length can be caused by incident gravitational wave radiation. LISA is sensitive to low-frequency gravitational waves not detectable with the ground-based LIGO interferometer.

LISA is designed to detect gravitational waves released by the coalescence of two supermassive black holes out to very high redshifts. In addition, it can measure the evolution of the gravity wave signal emitted as neutron stars or white dwarfs spiral into the supermassive black holes in the nuclei of galaxies. The details of the wave shapes are sensitive to general relativistic effects, so can be used to probe gravity in the strong field limit. Specifically, as a compact star is drawn toward a spinning supermassive black hole, LISA can measure the spin-induced precession of its orbit plane, providing a detailed mapping of space-time. Theoretical and numerical calculations of the predicted orbits and waveforms using general relativity will be critical to any interpretation of data from these observations.

Studies of strong gravity and matter in the extremes of temperature and density are identified goals of Constellation-X and LISA. Beyond these two missions there are many other fascinating opportunities. Many of these will require significant technology development to realize their objectives. For example, a space-based x-ray interferometer could directly image gas orbiting a black hole, tracing the gravitational field down to the event horizon. A sensitive x-ray polarimeter could probe QED in magnetic fields exceeding 10^{14} gauss, well above the QED critical field, where quantum effects become important. Under such conditions QED predicts strong dependence of polarization with x-ray wavelength, so the observations would provide a sensitive test of the predictions of QED. Sensitive hard x-ray and gamma-ray spectrometers could trace radioactive elements produced in supernova explosions, providing important constraints on theoretical models of the explosion and on the sites of nucleosynthesis. NASA is studying these advanced observatories to carry its program of probing the basic laws of physics into the future.

Among these future missions, an exciting prospect particularly relevant to this report is an advanced, space-based gravitational-wave detector designed to detect relic gravitational waves from the early universe. Inflation and phase transitions arising from symmetry breaking associated with electroweak, supersymmetry, or QCD phenomena leave their signatures in gravitational waves. Detection of these gravitational-wave signals could directly reveal how the forces, once unified, split off into the four separate forces we know today. LISA will probe for these signals down to the level where the background from galactic white-dwarf binaries dominates. A mission with multiple pairs of interferometers, designed to reject the galactic background and having a hundred- or thousandfold higher sensitivity than LISA will be required to reach the levels predicted by theory.

To achieve this very challenging goal, substantial technology development will be needed, aimed at optical readout for the gravitational reference sensors, high-power space-qualified lasers, laser stabilization systems, inexpensive, lightweight 3-meter-class optics, and improved micronewton thrusters. Equally important is the development of strategies and techniques for dealing with the astrophysical gravitational-wave signals that could hide the signal from the early universe. It is likely that support from more than one agency will be needed for both the advanced technical developments as well as the required computational and theoretical analyses.

UNDERSTANDING NATURE'S HIGHEST-ENERGY PARTICLES

The observation of particles in the universe with unexpectedly high energy raises several basic questions. What are the particles? Where do they come from? How did they achieve such high energies—many orders of magnitude higher than the output of the most powerful laboratory accelerators? Acceleration of particles to high energy is a characteristic feature of many energetic astrophysical sources, from solar flares and interplanetary shocks to galactic supernova explosions and distant active galaxies powered by accretion onto massive black holes. The signature of cosmic accelerators is that the accelerated electrons, protons, and heavier ions have a distribution of energies that extends far beyond the thermal distribution of particles in the source. It is the high energy that makes this population of naturally occurring particles of great interest, together with the fact that their energy density appears to be comparable to that of thermal gas and magnetic fields in their sources.

Primary cosmic-ray electrons, protons, and nuclei can produce secondary photons and neutrinos in or near the sources, which propagate over large distances in the universe undeflected by the magnetic fields that obscure the origins of their charged progenitors. Photons are produced by electrons, protons, and nuclei, while neutrinos are produced only by protons and nuclei. The proportions of the various types of particles, secondary and primary, thus reflect the nature of their sources. A unified approach to the problem therefore requires observations of the gamma rays and neutrinos as well as the cosmic rays.

Programs for more extensive measurements of high-energy gamma rays and the search for high-energy neutrinos are moving forward. They include STACEE, GLAST, and VERITAS for observation of gamma rays and IceCube to open the neutrino astronomy window. GLAST will be a space mission covering the gamma-ray energy range from 30 MeV to 300 GeV. VERITAS, a ground-based gamma-ray telescope, covers a complementary range from 100 GeV to 10 TeV. AMANDA is an operating neutrino telescope array deep in the south polar ice with an instrumented volume of about 2 percent of a cubic kilometer. IceCube is the planned cubic kilometer follow-on to AMANDA. NASA's HETE-2 satellite is currently monitoring the x-ray sky for gamma-ray bursts and detects about one burst every 2 weeks; the SWIFT satellite, currently scheduled to be launched in 2004, should detect a burst every day. STACEE is currently in operation; GLAST, VERITAS and IceCube are scheduled for operation and data taking in the second half of this decade. One promising source of high-energy particles of all types is the distant gamma-ray burst. EXIST is a wide-field-of-view instrument under study for launch near the end of the decade. All of the satellites will be able to provide the transient gamma-ray burst information needed to search for neutrino coincidences.

The primary cosmic ray spectrum as we observe it at Earth extends from mildly relativistic energies, where the kinetic energy is comparable to the rest mass of the particles, up to at least 10^{20} eV, a range of 11 orders of magnitude. The higher energy particles occur less frequently by about a factor of 50 for each power of 10 increase in energy. The abundant low-energy cosmic rays are accessible to relatively small, highly instrumented detectors that can be carried above the atmosphere to make precise measurements of the energy, charge, and mass of the particles. At higher energy, bigger (and therefore coarser) detectors are needed, and they must be exposed for long periods of time to collect a significant number of particles. At the highest energies, the intensity is on the order of one particle per square kilometer per century, so an effective collecting power of several thousand square kilometer years is needed.

In 1962 the MIT Volcano Ranch 10-square-kilometer air shower array recorded an event with an energy estimated at 10^{20} eV. Even now, this remains one of the dozen or so highest energy particles ever detected. Immediately after the discovery of the CMB in 1965, the potential importance of this event and its energy assignment was realized. If the sources of the highest energy cosmic rays are distributed uniformly throughout the universe, perhaps associated with quasars or other extremely powerful sources, then there should be a cutoff in the spectrum. This follows from the fact that a 10^{20} eV proton has enough energy to produce a pion when it interacts with a photon of the universal 2.7 K thermal background radiation. Further, the probability of this process is such that protons from distant extragalactic sources would lose a significant amount of energy in this way. Thus sources of particles with 10^{20} eV would have to be relatively nearby, comparable to the nearest active galaxies and quasars, for example. Since such nearby sources have not yet been identified, the problem remains unsolved, and it becomes crucial to obtain more data with improved measurement of energy.

The mystery of ultrahigh-energy cosmic rays has generated much speculation about their origin. Possible sites for cosmic accelerators include highly magnetized neutron stars, million-solar-mass black holes accreting matter at the centers of active galaxies, and jets from gamma-ray burst sources, possibly involving stellar-mass black holes. A problem for all these hypothetical mechanisms is that all calculations find it difficult to achieve per-particle energy as high as 10^{20} eV. Another possibility that has received serious attention is that the observed particles may instead be decay products of massive relics from the early universe—topological defects or very massive, unstable particles—so that no acceleration is needed. Even more exotic is the suggestion of a violation of Lorentz invariance at very high energy in such a way that the energy-loss mechanism in the microwave background is not effective, but this still leaves open the question of how such high energy was achieved in the first place.

The problem of the origin of the highest-energy cosmic rays has been the focus of a series of increasingly large air shower experiments of two types. One approach follows the original MIT design, a ground array of widely separated detectors that take a sparse sample of the particles in the shower front, typically far from its core. The detectors are simple and can be operated continuously, but such an array samples the shower at just one depth and only at distances far from the shower core, which contain less than 1 percent of the remaining cascade. Thus to assign energy to the events requires detailed and complicated calculations and is subject to fluctuations. The largest ground array at present is the 100 km^2 Akeno Giant Air Shower Array (AGASA) in Japan.

The second, complementary method uses the atmosphere as a calorimeter to find the energy of each event. Compact arrays of optical detectors look out to large distances and record the trail of fluorescence light generated by ionization of the atmosphere along the shower core. This has the advantage that most of the energy deposition is observed. A disadvantage is that it can operate only on clear, dark nights. In addition, the absolute energy assignment depends crucially on knowing the clarity of the atmosphere at the time of each event to infer the energy from the received signal. The High Resolution Fly's Eye Experiment (Hi-Res) in Utah uses this approach.

The most extensive data sets at present are those of AGASA and monocular Hi-Res, but a definitive picture of the ultrahigh-energy spectrum has yet to emerge. The problem is a combination of limited statistics and uncertainties in the energy assignment. The Hi-Res experiment can now operate in stereo, or binocular, mode. This should allow it gradually to accumulate more data with better determination of direction and energy because of the improved geometrical reconstruction of the shower axis that is possible with two "eyes."

A new experiment that combines both techniques, called the Auger Project, is under construction in Argentina. It is a 3,000-square-kilometer ground array that will include three fluorescence light detectors. It will therefore be able to cross-calibrate the two methods of measuring energy. Because of its size it will also accumulate significantly more statistics in the 10^{20} eV energy region than previous experiments. For these reasons, completion of this detector is crucial. The resources of several countries of the international Auger Project must come together to finish construction and bring the full array into operation by mid-decade. Eventually, pending the outcome of this investigation, it may be desirable to push to still higher energies with other detectors. A large ground-based detector complex in the northern hemisphere is being discussed, as is the possibility of observing a very large volume of atmosphere by looking down from space.

EXPLORING EXTREME PHYSICS IN THE LABORATORY

As discussed above, one scientific quest that lies solidly at the intersection of physics and astronomy is to extend the domain of physical conditions under which the fundamental laws have been tested and applied. In some cases we are providing checks on theories where we expect to find no surprises (although the history of physics warns us not to be too confident). In other instances, for example, in the study of high-density matter, heavy-element production, and ultrahigh-energy particle acceleration, we really do not understand how matter behaves and need experimental input to guide our physics. Having described how astronomical studies are expanding greatly our scientific horizons, the committee now looks at the other side of the coin and discusses how a complementary program of laboratory investigation in high-energy-density physics can push the application of physical principles into completely new territory.

The facilities that are needed for this research—lasers, magnetic confinement devices, and accelerators—have largely been (or are being) constructed for research in particle and nuclear physics, plasma fusion, and defense science. The challenge is to foster the growth of a new community of scientists who will creatively adapt these facilities for high-energy-density science. The NRC is engaged in a separate study on this field.[3]

Existing and planned laser facilities, notably the National Ignition Facility, can create transient pressures as high as a trillion atmospheres. They can

[3]The committee defers to that report for a more detailed description and more specific recommendations and limits its remarks to explaining the context while underscoring the relevance of that research to the physics of the universe. National Research Council, *Frontiers in High Energy Density Physics: The X-Games of Contemporary Science*, Washington, D.C., National Academies Press, 2003.

be used to create "mini fireballs" that expand into the surrounding plasma and may generate strong magnetic fields and form relativistic shock fronts. The temperature may be so high in this plasma that the protons, which carry the positive charge in conventional plasmas, can be replaced by positrons, just as is thought to occur in quasars, pulsars, and gamma-ray bursts. Another important use of lasers is to measure the wavelengths and strengths of the ultraviolet and x-ray atomic emission lines that have already been observed in astronomical sources by orbiting telescopes.

Magnetic confinement of hydrogen at temperatures approaching a hundred million degrees is one technique for causing nuclear fusion reactions in order to generate power. In addition, several experimental facilities have been constructed in which it is possible to squeeze plasma to tiny volumes and large pressures and to study how they behave. In particular, it should be possible to study turbulence and magnetic reconnection, which take place when magnetic field lines exchange partners. These are of central importance for understanding cosmic plasmas.

An example of a particle accelerator with appropriate capabilities is the Stanford Linear Accelerator Center, which creates intense beams of electrons with energy up to 50 GeV with micron-size cross sections. These beams can be used to create extremely energetic plasmas by focusing them onto solid targets. In addition, by "wiggling" electron beams using strong magnets, it is possible to create intense bursts of radiation throughout the spectrum similar to those thought to operate in astrophysical environments. Additionally, the RHIC facility at Brookhaven National Laboratory in New York is starting to delve into the world of extreme physics by colliding heavy ions with each other at relativistic speeds. The debris from these interactions is analyzed in detectors like those of particle physics.

Although it is possible to create some of the conditions of pressure and temperature found in cosmic sources, it is never going to be possible to reproduce these environments completely. What we can do and what is far more valuable is to use high-energy-density experiments to determine general rules for the behavior of matter. We want to better understand the rules that govern the rearrangement of magnetic structures, how fast electrons are heated and conduct energy in the presence of the collective plasma wave modes, how the pressure changes with density in ways that are relevant to interpreting observations of planets, stars, and supernovae, and how these processes dictate the behavior of shocks, magnetic reconnection, and turbulence. The challenge is to understand all of this physics in a generalizable, device-independent fashion so as to extrapolate and export our understanding to solve astrophysical problems. It is quite likely that this will be achieved by deriving universal scaling laws like those that are widely used in fluid dynamical investigations.

The field of high-energy-density physics is in its infancy. In order to fulfill its potential, it must draw in expertise from astrophysics, laser physics, magnetic confinement and particle beam research, numerical simulation, and atomic physics. It should attract younger scientists and help rejuvenate conventional plasma physics. It will require skillfully designed experiments that elucidate fundamental properties of plasmas. This will, in turn, require the development of far more sophisticated diagnostic devices to measure particle densities and speeds and to map dynamical magnetic fields. It will also require improved numerical simulations. Many of the facilities that will be used reside in large national laboratories. It is therefore important that outside users have access to these facilities for the purpose of designing, conducting, and analyzing major experiments.

STRIKING THE RIGHT BALANCE

In discussing the physics of the universe, one is naturally led to the extremes of scale—to the largest scales of the universe as a whole and to the smallest scales of elementary particles. Associated with this is a natural tendency to focus on the most extreme scale of scientific projects: the largest space observatories, the most energetic particle accelerators. However, our study of the physics of the universe repeatedly found instances where the key advances of the past or the most promising opportunities for the future come from work on a very different scale. Examples include laboratory experiments to test gravitational interactions, theoretical work and computer simulations to understand complex astrophysical phenomena, and small-scale detector development for future experiments. These examples are not intended to be exhaustive but to illustrate the need for a balanced program of research on the physics of the universe that provides opportunities for efforts that address the scientific questions but that do not necessarily fit within major program themes and their related large projects.

Two of our scientific questions—"Did Einstein have the last word on gravity?" and "Are there additional space-time dimensions?"—are being addressed by a number of laboratory and solar-system experiments to test the gravitational interaction. Tests of the principle of equivalence using laboratory torsion balances and lunar laser ranging could constrain hypothetical weakly coupled particles with long or intermediate range. These experiments have reached the level of parts in 10^{13} and could be improved by another order of magnitude. Improvement by a factor of around 10^5

could come from an equivalence principle test in space. While there are no robust predictions of violations of the equivalence principle at these levels, null experimental results provide important constraints on existing theories, and a positive signal would make for a scientific revolution.

Searches for deviations from the inverse square law of gravity at submillimeter scales could provide evidence that gravity leaks into macroscopic extra dimensions, or that additional light particles couple to matter with gravitational strength. Already, preliminary results rule out any violations greater than 1 percent of gravity down to half a millimeter and yield an upper limit of 0.2 mm on the size of the larger of two extra dimensions. Future experiments could improve the bounds in strength and distance scale by factors between 10 and 100. A balanced program should provide opportunities for such investigator-initiated projects.

Theoretical and computational work will play integral roles in addressing several of the scientific questions. To test whether Einstein had the last word on black holes will require analytically and numerically generated gravitational waveforms from black hole mergers that can be compared with gravitational-wave data. A better theoretical understanding of Type Ia supernovae is key to exploiting them as cosmological mileposts in the search for evidence of dark energy. In addition, fully three-dimensional numerical simulations of explosive nucleosynthesis during supernovae, including neutrino transport and armed with improved input data on nuclear reaction rates away from the line of nuclear stability, will be needed to address the production of the elements from iron to uranium. These simulations will require terascale computing capabilities. To infer the distribution and possible nature of dark matter from measurements of the development of structure in the universe, large-scale numerical simulations of the predictions of the different cold dark matter models are crucial. Numerical modeling of high-density plasma behavior will be key to revealing the scalable physical principles that can be invoked to understand high-energy astrophysical phenomena, such as the acceleration mechanisms for the highest energy particles. Numerical simulations of the Standard Model of quarks and gluons using lattice gauge theory are critical to understanding the nature of the transition from a quark-gluon plasma to hadrons in the early universe and the possible signatures of that event in gravitational-wave signals.

To realize fully the potential of high-performance computing to address these scientific questions will require a combination of access to the largest-scale computing facilities, resources for developing local, special-purpose computing clusters, development of simulation "collaboratories" that interconnect researchers and computers worldwide, and a new cadre of trained computational scientists to make use of these computing capabilities. The theoretical research that both underpins the simulations and interprets their outputs is also essential. While the committee does not have the expertise to make specific recommendations related to computational infrastructure, it strongly recommends that a balanced program of research on the physics of the universe include appropriate support for theory and computation.

A third example of small-scale effort with the potential to help realize many of our science objectives is research and development on advanced detectors. Examples include low-noise cryogenic instrumentation for future dark-matter searches, detectors for future microwave background polarization measurements, accelerometer development for future gravity and gravitational-wave measurements, advanced optical imagers, and x-ray polarimeters. Such modest investments could enable the next generation of discoveries. Yet oftentimes they are carried out by individual investigators or small teams not connected with a major ongoing program or mission, and they involve research based in one funding agency (the properties of certain solids) and application based in another (astronomical detectors). Such work sometimes fails to find a funding home. A balanced program on the physics of the universe should include mechanisms for detector R&D to support future experiments or observations.

RECOMMENDATIONS

The committee has identified timely opportunities for advancing our understanding of the universe and the laws that govern it. They range from understanding the birth and destiny of the universe to testing Einstein's theory of gravity in black holes and understanding the fundamental nature of matter, space, and time. In this chapter the next steps that must be taken to realize the opportunities are discussed.

No one agency currently has unique ownership of the science at the intersection of astronomy and physics; nor can one agency working alone mount the effort needed to realize the great opportunities. DOE, NASA, and NSF are all deeply interested in the science at this intersection, and each brings unique expertise to the enterprise. Only by working together can they take full advantage of the opportunities at this special time.

Coordination and joint planning are essential. In some instances, two of the agencies, or even all three, will need to work together. In others, one agency may be able to close the gap between the disciplines of physics and astronomy.

Finally, the committee's charge was to focus on DOE, NASA, and NSF. Although it does view the science in the larger context of activities around the world, the committee did not address the issue of international collaboration. The committee believes that the charge was sensible; absent a national plan for addressing science at the intersection of physics and astronomy, it will be difficult for the United States to pursue a coherent program of international collaboration. Likewise, the DOE, NASA, and NSF are the primary federal funding agencies with an interest in this interfacial science.

Some of the opportunities discussed involve international partners (e.g., LISA involves both NASA and the European Space Agency, Auger involves European and other American partners) or could involve them (e.g., an underground laboratory or a wide-field telescope in space). The strategy the committee has developed for DOE, NASA, and NSF should facilitate the participation of additional partners, be they international organizations, other agencies in the United States, or private foundations. Further, because U.S. scientists have been pioneers in recognizing the importance of this interdisciplinary science and in pursuing it, the committee believes it is likely that the United States can have a significant impact in this exciting science.

Recommendation on Understanding the Birth of the Universe

The cosmic microwave background radiation is a snapshot of the universe at a simpler time, some 400,000 years after its beginning. Important clues about the birth of the universe are encoded in the tiny variations of its intensity and its polarization. Already, CMB measurements have determined the shape of the universe, determined precisely the amount of ordinary matter, and given the first firm evidence for cosmic inflation. More discoveries will be made with the projects in place (e.g., MAP and Planck).

The portion of the polarization of the CMB that is produced by primordial gravitational waves offers great promise in testing further and understanding the inflationary era that may have occurred shortly after the birth of the universe. It is the clearest signature that inflation took place and reveals when it took place. Measuring this signature of inflation is extremely challenging and will require a significant R&D program before serious experimental efforts can be mounted. NASA, NSF, and DOE have played important roles in CMB discoveries so far, and the talents of all three agencies will be critical to the successful detection of the polarization signature of inflation.

- **Measure the polarization of the cosmic microwave background with the goal of detecting the signature of inflation. The committee recommends that NASA, NSF, and DOE undertake the research and development to bring the needed experiments to fruition.**

Recommendation on Understanding the Destiny of the Universe

Measurements of distant supernovae that indicate that the expansion of the universe is speeding up and not slowing down rank as one of the most important discoveries of the past quarter century. This accelerated expansion has revealed a new and mysterious energy form—dark energy—which accounts for two thirds of the matter and energy content of the universe. It has also changed how we view the destiny of our universe. Without understanding the properties of dark energy we cannot rule out an eventual recollapse or continued acceleration and an almost complete darkening of the sky in 150 billion years. Dark energy also raises questions about the fundamental nature of matter, space, and time. Because of the diffuse nature of dark energy, the universe is the primary laboratory in which it can be studied. By controlling the expansion rate, dark energy determines cosmic distances and affects the growth of structure in the universe. A host of experiments is on the horizon to probe dark energy through these effects.

To get at the nature of the dark energy will require a new class of large, wide-field (greater than 1 square degree) telescopes, both in space and on the ground. A wide-field, space-based telescope with a 2-meter mirror (such as SNAP) would provide crystal-clear images of large patches of the universe, ideal for deep gravitational lensing studies and for the discovery and follow-up of large numbers of supernovae out to high redshift ($z \sim 1.5$). A ground-based, wide-field telescope with an effective aperture of 6 to 8 meters (such as the LSST recommended by the Astronomy and Astrophysics Survey Committee) would rapidly image large portions of the sky, ideal for gravitational lensing studies and for the discovery of supernovae out to moderate redshift ($z \sim 0.7$). Both telescopes will also help to elucidate our understanding of the distribution of dark matter.

In this quest to solve one of the great puzzles of physics and astronomy, NASA and NSF have their traditional roles to play in space-based and ground-based astronomy, respectively. DOE also has an important role to play because of its contributions to the discovery of cosmic speed-up and its contributions to CCD detector development.

- **Determine the properties of dark energy. The committee supports the Large Synoptic Survey Telescope (LSST) project, which**

has significant promise for shedding light on dark energy. The committee further recommends that NASA and DOE work together to construct a wide-field telescope in space to determine the expansion history of the universe and fully probe the nature of dark energy.

Recommendation on Exploring the Unification of the Forces from Underground

Three of the committee's 11 questions—the nature of the dark matter, the question of neutrino masses, and the possible instability of the proton—must be addressed by carrying out experiments in a deep underground laboratory that is isolated from the constant bombardment of cosmic-ray particles. One of the most important discoveries in the past 10 years, that neutrinos have mass, was made in an underground laboratory. This discovery has implications for both the universe and the laws that govern it. The mass scale implied by measurements to date suggests that neutrinos contribute as much mass to the universe as do stars; and neutrino mass points to a grander theory that brings together the forces and particles of nature and may even shed light on the origin of ordinary matter.

The committee believes there are more opportunities for discovery at an underground laboratory. Experiments proposed for the near future to address the fundamental questions it has identified require depths up to 4,000 meters of water equivalent (mwe). More visionary experiments, as well as the long-term potential of such a laboratory to make discoveries, require even more shielding, to depths up to 6,000 mwe.

A laboratory for underground research must do more than provide shielded space. Many of the envisaged experiments require large, technically sophisticated, and costly detectors. An underground laboratory must also provide appropriate infrastructure to enable such experiments. Equally important is planning, selecting, and coordinating the experiments that carry out the science in the laboratory. DOE and NSF have some of the mechanisms in place (e.g., the SAGENAP process), but additional ones may be needed.

A North American laboratory with a depth significantly greater than 4,000 mwe and adequate infrastructure would be unique in the world and provide the opportunity for the United States to take a lead in "underground science" for decades. Such a laboratory might also be useful for carrying out important science in other disciplines, such as biology and geophysics.

- **Determine the neutrino masses, the constituents of dark matter, and the lifetime of the proton. The committee recommends that DOE and NSF work together to plan for and to fund a new generation of experiments to achieve these goals. It further recommends that an underground laboratory with sufficient infrastructure and depth be built to house and operate the needed experiments.**

Recommendation on Exploring the Basic Laws of Physics from Space

Our view of the universe has been transformed by the opening up of the whole electromagnetic spectrum, from low-frequency radio waves to high-energy gamma rays. The observable spectrum spans some 67 octaves, in contrast to the single octave that is visible to the eye. Most of the spectrum can only be observed from space. In recent years, NASA has recognized the potential of space observations to address questions that surround the basic laws of physics. The intellectual thrust of NASA's Beyond Einstein initiative aligns well with the science opportunities at the intersection of physics and astronomy, although not every project in it is relevant to the science opportunities the committee has identified. The committee supports NASA's strategic planning activity and the NRC's decadal survey as procedures for determining the highest priority initiatives in space astronomy. The charge of this committee was complementary: to examine the science opportunities at the intersection of physics and astronomy and to recommend a prioritized program to realize them.

Astronomy and Astrophysics in the New Millennium recently recommended two near-term missions described in the Beyond Einstein initiative, Constellation-X and LISA. Although it made these recommendations solely on the basis of the potential of the missions to address key questions in astronomy, these two missions also have great potential to address questions that lie at the boundary between physics and astronomy.

Constellation-X is a sensitive, high-resolution x-ray spectroscopy mission. Among its many potential targets are the gas disks orbiting black holes and the surfaces of neutron stars at nearly the speed of light, which will enable it to test general relativity and measure how matter behaves at high density.

LISA is a joint ESA-NASA project to measure low-frequency gravitational radiation from sources such as coalescing black holes and to undertake new tests of Einstein's theory. LISA will also be able to make an initial search for gravitational waves from the early universe, paving the way for future, more sensitive detectors that could possibly detect the gravitational whispers from inflation and other early universe sources.

NSF, with its experience in developing the ground-based LIGO detectors, and DOE, with its experience in optics and lasers, could play important roles in developing future gravitational-wave detectors in space.

> • **Use space to probe the basic laws of physics. The committee supports the Constellation-X and LISA missions, which have high promise for studying black holes and for testing Einstein's theory in new regimes. The committee further recommends that the agencies proceed with an advanced technology program to develop instruments capable of detecting gravitational waves from the early universe.**

Recommendation on Understanding Nature's Highest-Energy Particles

The particles with the highest observed energies are not produced by terrestrial accelerators but come to us from space. How and where they were accelerated to such energies is unknown but may involve gamma-ray bursters, massive black holes, or the decay of exotic objects produced in the early universe. Such particles offer the opportunity to explore physics at the highest energies. Significantly more and better data on the particles themselves are needed, as well as observations of high-energy gamma rays and searches for neutrinos associated with the same sources. A coordinated attack on the problem is essential. The elements of this program are in operation or scheduled for construction. They include GLAST, STACEE, and VERITAS for observation of gamma rays, AMANDA and IceCube to open the neutrino astronomy window, and Hi-Res and Auger for study of the highest-energy cosmic rays.

The Southern Auger detector, in Argentina, is in its early phases of construction by an international collaboration with strong U.S. involvement and leadership. Completion and multiyear operation of the hybrid Auger detector is crucial because it can look at the highest-energy cosmic rays using two independent techniques, thereby providing cross calibration for detectors operating in the northern hemisphere using only one or the other technique. In addition, the Auger array will extend coverage to the southern sky.

On the horizon are a larger ground-based detector complex in the northern hemisphere and proposals for large field-of-view observations from space of giant cosmic-ray air showers. The data that will be collected from the projects now in place are crucial for defining the science questions that will underpin the newer projects.

- **Determine the origin of the highest-energy gamma rays, neutrinos, and cosmic rays. The committee supports the broad approach already in place and recommends that the United States ensure the timely completion and operation of the Southern Auger array.**

Recommendation on Exploring Physics Under Extreme Conditions in the Laboratory

Astronomical telescopes provide glimpses of extreme physical environments under conditions that can never be replicated or probed experimentally on Earth. They challenge laboratory physicists to devise and perform experiments that will uncover the physical principles that can be scaled up to understand the most powerful astronomical sources, like quasars, neutron stars, supernova explosions, gamma-ray bursts, and the big bang. Conversely, observation of these astronomical phenomena can provide remote data points to bolster our understanding of these principles and to suggest new insights directly relevant to terrestrial investigations—a service that astronomy has been providing to physics for centuries.

Although the field of high-energy-density experimentation is in its infancy, the capability will soon be at hand to push our understanding of condensed matter and plasma physics into regimes unimaginable a decade ago.[4] One immediate challenge is to improve our understanding of the generic, global properties of plasmas under a broad range of conditions not specialized to the program to achieve fusion. It is intended to carry out these physics experiments over a wide range of conditions, using powerful lasers, electron beams, and magnetic pinch facilities. Another use of these plasma research facilities is to expand our measurements of the important spectral lines and opacities needed to interpret observations with ultraviolet and x-ray telescopes and to model cosmic explosions. The key to taking advantage of these unique facilities is to bring together a diverse group of scientists working in different disciplines and supported by different agencies.

- **Discern the physical principles that govern extreme astrophysical environments through the laboratory study of high-energy-**

---

[4]Another NRC committee, chaired by R. Davidson, has been charged with surveying this field, and this committee will defer to it for detailed programmatic advice.

density physics. The committee recommends that the agencies cooperate in bringing together the different scientific communities that can foster this rapidly developing field.

Recommendation on an Interagency Initiative on the Physics of the Universe

The committee has identified opportunities for major advances in our understanding of the birth and destiny of the universe and the fundamental laws that govern matter, space, and time. The opportunities lie at the intersection of a number of physics and astronomy disciplines and span the responsibilities of DOE, NASA, and NSF. While many opportunities have evolved from the existing programs of these agencies, these opportunities now transcend those programs, requiring combinations of expertise (e.g., particle accelerators and detectors and space experimentation) that are currently maintained by different agencies or by different disciplines within one of them.

If the opportunities before us are to be realized, the three agencies must work together both in planning and in implementation. There are already a number of examples where such cooperation has succeeded, such as the Sloan Digital Sky Survey (NSF, DOE, and NASA), the Cryogenic Dark Matter Search (NSF and DOE), the BOOMERanG and MAXIMA cosmic microwave background experiments (NASA and NSF), and new initiatives just under way, including the Large Hadron Collider (DOE and NSF) and GLAST (NASA and DOE). Valuable lessons in management, coordination, and funding have been learned from these projects.

No program in DOE, NASA, or NSF provides ongoing stewardship for, or funding of, the full breadth of this new field. Further, the talents and unique capabilities of all three agencies are required for progress to be made.

- **Realize the scientific opportunities at the intersection of physics and astronomy. The committee recommends establishment of an interagency initiative on the physics of the universe, with the participation of DOE, NASA, and NSF. This initiative should provide structures for joint planning and mechanisms for joint implementation of cross-agency projects.**

Such an initiative can realize many of the special scientific opportunities that this report has described, but not within the budgets of the three agencies as they stand. The answer is not simply to trim existing programs to make room for these new initiatives. Many of the existing programs in astronomy and in physics are also critical to answering the 11 questions, as outlined in the first section of this chapter. Other programs address exciting and timely questions within physics and astronomy separately. New funds will be needed to realize the grand opportunities before us.

In addition, the committee believes that it is essential that an inter-agency initiative on the physics of the universe maintain a balanced approach that provides opportunities for investigator-initiated experiments, detector R&D, theoretical work, and computational efforts that address the committee's scientific questions but that do not necessarily fit within major program themes and their related large projects. Our understanding of the physics of the universe is often advanced by large projects, such as space observatories, particle-physics laboratories, or ground-based observation efforts. Indeed, most of the committee's recommendations involve large projects. However, because the physics of the universe is interdisciplinary in character, significant advances can emerge from work carried out at the interface between fields. Often this work involves small-scale efforts, such as table-top experiments and detector development, or computational science and theory. Unlike many large-scale projects, some small-scale efforts are able to respond on a short time scale to address specific but important scientific questions.

Remarkable advances have been made in the past two decades in our understanding of the basic constituents of matter and the forces that shape them. These advances, as well as technological breakthroughs, now present an unprecedented opportunity to answer some of the most fundamental questions that mankind can ask. Progress in addressing the fundamentals of matter, space, and time and progress in understanding the birth of the universe are now inextricably linked, so that astronomers and physicists as well as the agencies that fund them must work together more closely than ever before. The Committee on the Physics of the Universe believes that this is possible, and further, that if its recommendations are implemented, the next two decades could see a significant transformation of our understanding of the origin and fate of the universe, of the laws that govern it, and even of our place within it.

Appendixes

A

Meeting Agendas

FIRST MEETING

March 15–16, 2000
National Academy of Sciences
Washington, D.C.

Wednesday, March 15

Open session

9:00 am   Convene; welcome; introductions
                —Michael Turner, Chair
9:30   Background: From "Inner Space—Outer Space" at Fermilab to the
          BPA Forum
                —Michael Turner, Chair
10:00   Preliminary Study Plan—Science Topics
          Looking Inward to See Outward and Outward to See Inward
                —Helen Quinn, Stanford Linear Accelerator Center and David
                   Spergel, Princeton
          Fundamental Aspects of Gravity
                —Frank Wilczek, Massachusetts Institute of Technology
          The Composition of the Universe
                —Sandra Faber, University of California at Santa Cruz (by telephone)
          The Cosmic Laboratory and Astroengineering
                —Roger Blandford, California Institute of Technology
12:00 noon Lunch
1:00 pm   Agency Perspectives
          National Aeronautics and Space Administration
                —Alan Bunner
          National Science Foundation
                —Robert Eisenstein
          Department of Energy
                —Peter Rosen

Closed session

2:00   Astronomy and Astrophysics Survey Committee (AASC) recommendations
                —Joseph Taylor, Princeton

Open session

2:30   Status of the AASC
                —Joseph Taylor, Princeton
3:00   Break
3:15   Cosmic Genesis Workshop—Connections: From Quarks to Cosmos
                —Rocky Kolb, Fermilab
4:00   AASC Panel on Particle, Nuclear, and Gravitational-Wave Astrophysics
                —Tom Gaisser, University of Delaware, Bartol Research Institute
            Physics Survey
            Elementary Particle Physics
                —Bruce Winstein, University of Chicago
            Gravitational Physics
                —Clifford Will, Washington University
5:00   Discussion
                —Michael Turner, Chair
5:30   Adjourn for the day

Thursday, March 16

Closed session

9:00 am   Reconvene; study plan; discussion; future plans
                —Michael Turner, Chair
2:30 pm   Adjourn

SECOND MEETING

June 6–7, 2000
Rochester, New York

This meeting was closed in its entirety.

Tuesday, June 6

10:00 am   Convene; update
               —Michael Turner, Chair
10:30   Discussion of draft report (presentations and critiques)
               —Full committee
5:30   Adjourn for the day

Wednesday, June 7

9:00 am   Reconvene; discussion of connections to other disciplines,
institutional/agency issues; writing assignments
               —Michael Turner, Chair
1:30 pm   Adjourn

THIRD MEETING

October 19–20, 2000
Chicago, Illinois

This meeting was closed in its entirety.

Thursday, October 19

1:00 pm   Convene
Discussion of full Phase 1 draft report
               —Michael Turner, Chair
7:00   Adjourn for the day

Friday, October 20

8:00 am   Reconvene; action items for completing draft report for review
               —Michael Turner, Chair
1:00 pm   Schedule for preparing review draft; discussion of plans for Phase 2;
dissemination of Phase 1 results
               —Michael Turner, Chair
7:30   Adjourn

FOURTH MEETING

May 1–2, 2001
Washington, D.C.

Tuesday, May 1

Closed session

12:00 noon Convene; introduction of new members; balance and composition
            discussion; Phase 2 plans
                —Michael Turner, Chair

Open session

2:20 pm   Public introductions; Phase 2 process
              —Michael Turner, Chair
2:30   National Underground Laboratory Effort
          Solar Neutrinos: Current Status
              —John Bahcall, Institute for Advanced Study
3:50   Break
4:00   Overview of Non-Solar Neutrino Theory/Experiments
          Primer on Current Understanding of Origins of Elements above Iron
              —Wick Haxton, University of Washington
5:00   Observatory of Multiflavor Neutrinos from Supernovae (OMNIS)
              —Richard Boyd, The Ohio State University
5:35   Oak Ridge Electron Linear Accelerator (ORELA)
              —Paul Koehler, Oak Ridge National Laboratory
6:10   Oak Ridge National Laboratory for Neutrino Detectors (ORLaND)
              —George Fuller, University of California at San Diego
              —Frank Avignone, University of South Carolina
6:45   Adjourn for the day

Wednesday, May 2

Closed session

8:00 am   Committee discussion
              —Michael Turner, Chair

Open session

9:30   Rare Isotope Accelerator
              —Hendrik Schatz, Michigan State University

10:30	Break
11:00	Underground Nucleon Decay and Neutrino Observatory
	—Chang Kee Jung, State University of New York at-Stony Brook
12:00 noon	Lunch
1:00 pm	CryoArray
	—Dan Akerib, Case Western Reserve University
1:35	n-nbar Search (rescheduled to July meeting)
	—Yuri Kamyshkov, University of Tennessee
2:10	Origin of the Heavy Elements in Stellar Explosions: Holifield Radioactive Ion Beam Facility
	—Michael Smith, Oak Ridge National Laboratory
2:45	Summary Talk on the Major Double Beta Decay Experiments Proposed for the Underground Lab
	—Steve Elliott, University of Washington
3:45	Break

Closed session

4:00	Committee discussion; examples of interagency cooperation; future plans; writing assignments
	—Michael Turner, Chair
5:30	Adjourn

FIFTH MEETING

June 6–7, 2001
Pasadena, California

Wednesday, June 6

Closed session

8:00 am	Convene; review of writing submissions; goals/plans for this meeting
	—Michael Turner, Chair

Open session

Numerical Nuclear Astrophysics

9:00	Nucleosynthesis overview
	—Stan Woosley, University of California at Santa Cruz
10:00	Break

Cosmic Journeys–Overview and Missions

10:30	Introduction; context; science overview
	—Nick White, NASA/Goddard Space Flight Center

11:00   Gravity Waves
              —Sterl Phinney, California Institute of Technology
11:30   Strong-Field Gravity
              —Mitch Begelman, University of Colorado/JILA
12:00 noon Lunch
1:00 pm   Nuclear Equation of State; High-Field QED
              —Jeremy Heyl, Center for Astrophysics
1:30   Gamma-Ray Bursts
              —Neil Gehrels, NASA/Goddard Space Flight Center
2:00   Summary; proposed mission overview; technology program
              —Nick White
2:30   Break

Plasma Laboratory Astrophysics
3:00   NRC High Energy Density Plasma Physics Study
              —Ron Davidson, Princeton University (via telephone)
3:15   Science Overview; Funding Gaps
              —Dave Arnett, University of Arizona
4:15   High-Energy-Density Physics
              —Bruce Remington, Lawrence Livermore National Laboratory
4:45   Explosions
              —Edison Liang, Rice University
5:15   Mildly Relativistic Plasmas
              —R. Paul Drake, University of Michigan

High-Performance Computing
5:45   Broad Future National Needs for Science at the Interface of Physics
          and Astronomy
              —Michael Norman, University of California at San Diego
6:15   Adjourn for the day

Thursday, June 7

Closed session

8:00 am   Convene; review of Wednesday's presentations
              —Michael Turner, Chair

Open session

Lessons from an Interagency Project
9:00   GLAST: Opportunities and Difficulties of Interagency Cooperation
          (DOE/NASA)
              —Peter Michelson, Stanford University

10:00 am   Break

CMB Polarization [B-modes]
10:30   Overview of Possible Future Projects and Missions
                    —Bruce Winstein, University of Chicago

Closed session

11:30   Working lunch; future plans; continue review of writing submissions
                 to date; future writing assignments
                    —Michael Turner, Chair
1:00 pm   Adjourn

SIXTH MEETING

July 13–15, 2001
Snowmass, Colorado

Friday, July 13

Closed session

8:00 am   Convene; goals/plans for this meeting
                    —Michael Turner, Chair

Open session

9:00   VERITAS Update
                    —Trevor Weekes, Harvard Smithsonian CfA
9:30   n-nbar Search
                    —Yuri Kamyshkov, University of Tennessee
10:00   The Search for the Axion
                    —Leslie Rosenberg, Massachusetts Institute of Technology
10:30   Break
11:00   U.S. Involvement in the Large Hadron Collider
                    —John Peoples, Sloan Digital Sky Survey
11.30   Telescope Array Project
                    —Masaki Fukushima, University of Tokyo
12:00 noon Lunch
1:00 pm   The Implications of Export Control Policies on International
                 Cooperation
                    —Eugene Skolnikoff, Chair, NRC International Space Programs
                       Committee (by telephone)

Wide-Field Telescopes

1:30   Large-Aperture Synoptic Survey Telescope
                   —Chris Stubbs, University of Washington
                   —Tony Tyson, Bell Labs/Lucent Technologies
2:30   Supernova Acceleration Probe
                   —Saul Perlmutter, Lawrence Berkeley National Laboratory
3:30   Break
4:00   P-mode Oscillation Imager
                   —Nick Kaiser, University of Hawaii
5:00   Discussion of Wide-Field Telescopes
                   —Michael Turner, Chair
6:00   Adjourn for the day

Saturday, July 14

Closed session

1:00 pm   Convene; review of Friday's presentations
                   —Michael Turner, Chair

Open session

1:30   Low-Energy Solar Neutrinos
                   —Hamish Robertson, University of Washington
              Discussion of Low-Energy Solar Neutrinos
                   —Michael Turner, Chair
3:00   Break

High-Energy Cosmic Rays

3:30   Auger
                   —Paul Sommers, University of Utah
4:00   IceCube
                   —Francis Halzen, University of Wisconsin
4:30   Orbiting Wide-Angle Light-Collectors
                   —Robert Streitmatter, NASA/Goddard Space Flight Center
5:00   Discussion of High-Energy Cosmic Rays
                   —Michael Turner, Chair

Closed session

5:30   Review of the day's presentations; priorities for Sunday
                   —Michael Turner, Chair
6:00   Adjourn for the day

Sunday, July 15

Open session

8:00 am   Convene; Review of past interagency efforts
            Sloan Digital Sky Survey (SDSS)
                    —John Peoples, Sloan Digital Sky Survey
8:30   Cryogenic Dark Matter Search (CDMS)
                    —Bernard Sadoulet, University of California at Berkeley
9:00   Discussion on SDSS and CDMS
                    —Michael Turner, Chair
9:30   Break

Closed session

9:45   Review of presentations at this meeting; plan of action for final phase;
            review of writing assignments; assignments for next meeting
                    —Michael Turner, Chair
11:00   Adjourn

SEVENTH MEETING

November 29–30, 2001
Chicago, Ilinois

This meeting was closed in its entirety.

Thursday, November 29

8:00 am   Convene; goals and plan for the meeting; bias discussion
                    —Michael Turner, Chair
8:25   Small-Scale Gravitational Physics Experiments
                    —Eric Adelberger, University of Washington
9:25   Review of High-Energy Density Laboratory Astrophysics Efforts
            and Their Relationship to Q2C Science
                    —Roger Blandford, California Institute of Technology
10:25   Break
10:45   Review of original charge to the committee and the intended
            audience(s) for the report; discussion and drafting of findings and
            recommendations
                    —Michael Turner, Chair
6:00 pm   Adjourn for the day

Friday, November 30

8:00 am   Reconvene; finalize findings and recommendations; finalize straw person outline for the full report; writing assignments for drafting full text; future plans and schedule
        —Michael Turner, Chair

2:00 pm   Adjourn

EIGHTH MEETING

January 27–28, 2002
Irvine, California

This meeting was closed in its entirety.

Sunday, January 27

8:30 am   Convene; goals and agenda for meeting; resolve outstanding issues; finalize recommendations; group critique of full draft report
        —Michael Turner, Chair

6:00 pm   Adjourn for the day

Monday, January 28

8:30 am   Writing groups convene individually to work on draft

11:00   Reconvene; discuss science updates for old Phase 1 chapters; outstanding issues; future goals and time line; dissemination efforts
        —Michael Turner, Chair

5:30 pm   Adjourn

B

Call for Community Input

The call for community input, which is excerpted below, was issued in March 2001 as an American Astronomical Society electronic bulletin. The call for input was also presented at several physics meetings in early 2001.

The NRC's Committee on the Physics of the Universe (CPU) was charged by DOE, NASA, and NSF with identifying science opportunities at the intersection of physics and astronomy and recommending strategies for realizing these science opportunities. The NRC has recently issued the Phase I CPU report: Connecting Quarks with the Cosmos: 11 Science Questions for the New Century. The report is available on-line in its entirety at http://www.nas.edu/bpa/reports/cpu/index.html.

The Committee believes that there are extraordinary opportunities for breakthroughs in our understanding of the Universe in which we live and the fundamental laws which govern it. We are beginning the critical second phase of our activity. The goal of Phase II is to identify strategies for realizing the 11 timely science opportunities. This will include making recommendations on how the agencies can most effectively cooperate and coordinate their programs in this area and identifying a set of projects that can realize the opportunities identified in the Phase I report.

The CPU needs and seeks input from the broad community of astronomers and physicists on agency cooperation/coordination issues and projects to realize the opportunities before us. We also welcome advice on any other aspect of implementing the Connecting Quarks with the Cosmos science. Comments should be sent to q2c@nas.edu.

The CPU is especially interested in being informed about specific projects (experimental or theoretical) that directly address any of the 11 science questions identified in the Phase I report.

We encourage astronomers and physicists to tell us about ideas and projects, from new concepts to relatively mature experimental and observational proposals. We ask that such descriptions be sent to q2c@nas.edu. These informal descriptions should be no longer than 2 pages and should contain:

1. Name of contact person and contact information
2. Discussion of the scientists who will or might be involved
3. Description of project and techniques used, list of key technical challenges and any new technologies requiring R&D

4. Rough estimate of cost and schedule

5. Description of the science questions that will be addressed and, to the extent possible, the science reach

6. Discussion of plans for or potential/need for multi-agency involvement

Based upon the information received, the CPU will invite presentations of projects that have significant potential to address our 11 science questions at upcoming CPU meetings associated with the APS April meeting in Washington, DC, the AAS June meeting in Pasadena, the Snowmass meeting in July and further meetings to be announced.

The Phase I report will be presented at a public session at the April APS meeting and members of the CPU will be present to answer questions and receive comments. The following are the 11 science opportunities identified in "Connecting Quarks with the Cosmos:"

- What is the dark matter?
- What are the masses of the neutrinos, and how have they shaped the evolution of the universe?
- Are there additional space-time dimensions?
- What is the nature of the dark energy?
- Are protons unstable?
- How did the universe begin?
- Did Einstein have the last word on gravity?
- How do cosmic accelerators work and what are they accelerating?
- Are there new states of matter at exceedingly high density and temperature?
- Is a new theory of matter and light needed at the highest energies?
- How were the elements from iron to uranium made?

A more complete description of the questions and their context is contained in the Phase I report (available at *http://www.nas.edu/bpa/reports/cpu/index.html*).

Current members of the CPU are:

Michael S. Turner, The University of Chicago, *Chair*
Roger D. Blandford, California Institute of Technology
Sandra M. Faber, University of California at Santa Cruz
Thomas K. Gaisser, University of Delaware
Fiona Harrison, California Institute of Technology
John P. Huchra, Harvard University
Helen R. Quinn, Stanford Linear Accelerator Center
R. G. Hamish Robertson, University of Washington
Bernard Sadoulet, University of California at Berkeley
Frank J. Sciulli, Columbia University
David N. Spergel, Princeton University
J. Anthony Tyson, Lucent Technologies
Frank A. Wilczek, Massachusetts Institute of Technology
Clifford Will, Washington University, St. Louis
Bruce D. Winstein, The University of Chicago

C

Project Proposals Received
(Listed Chronologically)

1. Investigations of the Physical Consequences of Torsion, Richard Hammond, North Dakota State University

2. The DEEP2 Redshift Survey, Marc Davis, University of California at Berkeley

3. Nucleosynthesis of the Elements—All of Them, Stan Woosley, University of California at Santa Cruz

4. The Baryonic Dark Matter Telescope, Rudolph Schild, Harvard-Smithsonian Center for Astrophysics

5. Department of Energy–NASA Laboratory Plasma Astrophysics Collaboration, Robert Heeter, Lawrence Livermore National Laboratory

6. Fermilab Neutrino Experiments, Fritz DeJongh, Fermi National Accelerator Laboratory

7. OMNIS, the Observatory of Multiflavor Neutrinos from Supernovae, Richard Boyd, Ohio State University

8. Cosmic Accelerators in the Laboratory, in Theory, and in Observations, R. Paul Drake, University of Michigan

9. Reactor-Based Search for Neutron–Anti-Neutron Transitions, Yuri Kamyshkov, University of Tennessee

10. Oak Ridge Electron Linear Accelerator: How Were the Elements from Iron to Uranium Made?, Paul Koehler, Oak Ridge National Laboratory

11. Pierre Auger Cosmic Ray Observatory Project, J.W. Cronin, University of Chicago

12. Cosmological Explorer Mission, Rodger Thompson, University of Arizona

13. Recreating Planetary Cores in the Laboratory, Gilbert Collins, Lawrence Livermore National Laboratory

14. Laser Interferometer Space Antenna Mission, Thomas Prince, California Institute of Technology

15. Octonions and Fermions, Corinne A. Manogue and Tevian Dray, Oregon State University

16. Origin of the Heavy Elements in Stellar Explosions, Michael Smith, Oak Ridge National Laboratory

17. The Very Energetic Radiation Imaging Telescope Array System, Trevor Weekes, Harvard-Smithsonian Center for Astrophysics

18. A Unified Quantum Theory of Quark-Space-Time Structure, David Finkelstein, Georgia Institute of Technology

19. IceCube, Francis Halzen, University of Wisconsin

20. Molecular Clouds and Star Forming Regions in Laser Experiments, ASCI Simulations, Theory, and Observations, Jave Kane, Lawrence Livermore National Laboratory

21. The TeraScale Supernova Initiative, Anthony Mezzacappa, Oak Ridge National Laboratory

22. Tests of String Theory Using Gravitational Wave Detectors, Benjamin Harms, University of Alabama

23. CryoArray, Dan Akerib, Case Western Reserve University, and Rick Gaitskell, University College London

24. The Panoramic Optical Imager, Rolf-Peter Kudritzki and Nick Kaiser, University of Hawaii

25. The Large-Aperture Synoptic Survey Telescope, Tony Tyson, Bell Labs, Lucent Technologies

26. The Constellation X-ray Mission, Nicholas White, NASA's Goddard Space Flight Center, and Harvey Tananbaum, Smithsonian Astrophysical Observatory

27. Micro-arcsecond X-ray Imaging Mission, Webster Cash, University of Colorado, and Nicholas White, NASA's Goddard Space Flight Center

28. SuperNova/Acceleration Probe, Michael Levi and Saul Perlmutter, Lawrence Berkeley National Laboratory

29. Center for Plasma Astrophysics, Eric Blackman, University of Rochester

30. National Underground Science Laboratory, John Bahcall, Institute for Advanced Study, Wick Haxton, University of Washington, and Marvin Marshak, University of Minnesota

31. Generating Neutron Star Atmospheres on Petawatt Lasers with Ultra-High Magnetic Fields, Richard Klein, Lawrence Livermore National Laboratory and University of California at Berkeley

32. The Oak Ridge Laboratory for Neutrino Detectors, Jim Beene, Oak Ridge National Laboratory

33. Gamma Ray Bursts in the Laboratory: Electron-Positron Fireball Production with Super Intense Lasers, Todd Ditmire, University of Texas at Austin

34. Lunar Laser Ranging and Gravitational Physics, James Williams, Jet Propulsion Laboratory

35. High-Temperature Astrophysical Plasma Opacity Research, Paul Springer, Lawrence Livermore National Laboratory

36. Underground Nucleon Decay and Neutrino Observatory, Chang Kee Jung, State University of New York at Stony Brook

37. The Dynamics of Supernovae and Supernova Remnants, Bruce Remington, Lawrence Livermore National Laboratory

38. High Mach Number Jets in Astrophysics and in the Laboratory, Adam Frank, University of Rochester

39. The Majorana Project: Probing Effective Neutrino Mass with ^{76}Ge Neutrinoless Double-Beta Decay, Harry Miley, Pacific Northwest National Laboratory, and Ludwig De Braeckeleer, Duke University

40. Next Generation X-ray Timing Mission, Tod Strohmayer, NASA's Goddard Space Flight Center

41. Orbiting Wide-Angle Light Collectors, Robert Streitmatter, NASA's Goddard Space Flight Center

42. The Molybdenum Observatory of Neutrinos Project for Low-Energy Neutrino Physics, H. Ejiri, Osaka University, and R.G.H. Robertson, University of Washington

43. Energetic X-ray Imaging Survey Telescope, Josh Grindlay, Harvard-Smithsonian Center for Astrophysics

44. Interplanetary Ranging and Gravitational Physics, John Anderson and James Williams, Jet Propulsion Laboratory

45. WIMP Dark Matter Search, Tom Ward, Department of Energy

46. HElium:Roton Observation of Neutrinos, Robert Lanou, Brown University

47. MiniBooNE Experiment, Rex Tayloe, Indiana University Cyclotron Facility

48. Neutrons for Astrophysics Research, Michael Snow, Indiana University Cyclotron Facility

49. Probing Nucleonic Substructure with the STAR Detector Using Polarized Proton Collisions at RHIC, Steven Vigdor, Indiana University

50. Proton and Ion Energy Losses in Hot, Dense Plasma, Pravesh Patel, Lawrence Livermore National Laboratory

51. The DRIFT Project: A Direction-Sensitive Detector for WIMP Dark Matter, C.J. Martoff, Temple University

52. New Detectors for "Underground Physics," William Willis, Columbia University

53. Supersensitive Liquid Xenon Experiment for Direct Dark Matter Detection, Elena Aprile and Chuck Hailey, Columbia University

54. End Game of Solar Neutrinos: The Proton-Proton Program, R.S. Raghavan, Bell Laboratories, Lucent Technologies

55. A Dedicated Facility for Laboratory Astrophysics Using High Intensity Particle and Photon Beams, Pisin Chen, Stanford Linear Accelerator Center

56. The Rare Isotope Accelerator, Michael Wiescher, University of Notre Dame, Hendrik Schatz, Michigan State University, and Guy Savard, Argonne National Laboratory

57. Microarcsecond Imaging of Jets and Black Holes at Gamma-Ray Energies with Fresnel Lens Optics, Neil Gehrels, NASA's Goddard Space Flight Center, and Gerald K. Skinner, Centre d'Etude Spatiale des Rayonnements

58. High Pressure Solar Neutrino Time Projection Chamber Detector, Giovanni Bonvicini, Wayne State University

59. Astrophysical Simulation Institute, Wai-Mo Suen, Washington University

60. Fundamental Physics from High-Precision Lunar Laser-Ranging, T. Murphy, Jr., E. Adelberger, C. Stubbs, and J. Strasburg, University of Washington, K. Nordtvedt, Northwest Analysis, J. Williams and J. Dickey, Jet Propulsion Laboratory

61. HYBRID Neutrino Detector, Kenneth Lande, University of Pennsylvania

D

Glossary and Acronyms

accretion, accretion disk: the process by which gas flows around and onto a compact gravitating object. Astronomical objects as diverse as protostars and active galaxies may derive their energy from the gravitational power released by the infall, or accretion, of material onto a central object. The combined effects of gravity and rotation often force the accreting material into an orbiting accretion disk.

active galactic nucleus (AGN): the term active galactic nucleus refers to the existence of energetic phenomena in the nuclei, or central regions, of galaxies that cannot be attributed clearly and directly to stars.

air shower: when a high-energy particle enters Earth's atmosphere, the initial particle interacts with air atoms, producing many new particles. In turn, the newly produced particles produce additional particles. Some of the particles penetrate to Earth's atmosphere. The resulting effect is known as an air shower.

ALICE: a collaboration that is building a dedicated heavy-ion detector to exploit the unique physics potential of nucleus-nucleus interactions at LHC energies. The aim is to study the physics of strongly interacting matter at extreme energy densities, where the formation of a new phase of matter, the quark-gluon plasma, can occur.

anisotropy: dependence of the properties of a system on the orientation or direction of observation. The distribution of galaxies in space is not uniform, whereas the intensity of the cosmic background radiation from the big bang is highly uniform in all directions—i.e., it is almost isotropic. Astronomers are using sensitive telescopes to study the small anisotropies in the cosmic background radiation that should be present given the nonuniform distribution of galaxies.

antimatter: matter composed of antiparticles (e.g., antiprotons, antineutrons, antielectrons) instead of particles (e.g., protons, neutrons, electrons).

antiparticle: Counterpart to a particle with properties identical to those of the particle except that the antiparticle's electrical charge and a few other properties are opposite those of the particle. When a particle and its antiparticle meet, they can annihilate each other.

arcsecond: a unit of angle corresponding to 1/3600th of a degree. An arcsecond is approximately the size of a dime viewed from the distance of 1 mile.

axion: a hypothetical elementary particle whose existence might explain certain particle physics experiments; a candidate for cold dark matter.

B meson: meson that contains one *b* quark and one *u*, *d*, or *s* antiquark.

B factory: specialized accelerator facility that produces large numbers of B mesons.

baryon: a massive, strongly interacting elementary particle, such as a proton or a neutron. Ordinary matter as we know it consists largely of baryons.

big bang: the theory that the universe began with all matter and energy concentrated to very high density and temperature some 13 billion years ago. The present universe expanded from that epoch and is still expanding.

big bang nucleosynthesis: the process by which during the first 3 minutes after the big bang, protons and neutrons fused together to form the nuclei of the lightest elements in the periodic table, hydrogen, deuterium, helium, and lithium. The relative abundance of these elements, particularly deuterium, is sensitive to the density of ordinary matter and provides the first method for estimating the amount of baryonic matter.

binary companion: a star that is gravitationally bound to another star. Binary companions orbit around their common center of gravity. A high proportion, perhaps one-half, of all stars in the Milky Way galaxy are binaries or members of more complex multiple systems.

binary pulsar: a radio pulsar (q.v.) that is gravitationally bound to a companion star and orbits it. The signals from such a system can be used to test some aspects of general relativity to great precision.

black hole: a region of space where the gravitational pull is so strong that, classically, nothing can escape. The boundary of this region is called the black hole's event horizon (q.v.). Black holes can form when a massive star undergoes gravitational collapse (q.v.).

BOOMERanG: the Balloon Observation Of Millimeteric Extragalactic Radiation and Geophysics (BOOMERanG) maps the cosmic microwave background (CMB) using a balloon-borne telescope that circumnavigates Antarctica. The data gathered are analyzed to create images of the early universe, test models of cosmology, and measure fundamental cosmological parameters such as the overall density of the universe.

Bose-Einstein particles or bosons: subatomic particle with integral spin (i.e., angular momentum in quantum-mechanical units of 0, 1, etc.). Bosons, unlike fermions, do not obey the exclusion principle. Many bosons can occupy the same quantum state. Photons, gluons, pi-mesons, and nuclei of even mass number are all bosons.

CDMS, CDMS II: the Cryogenic Dark Matter Search is a federally funded project involving some 50 scientists from 10 U.S. institutions in the search for the nature of dark matter.

Cerenkov radiation: electromagnetic radiation (usually visible light) emitted by a charged particle when it passes through matter at a velocity exceeding that of light in the material.

CERN: European Organization for Nuclear Research (originally the European Center for Nuclear Research), located near Geneva, Switzerland.

Chandra x-ray satellite observatory (formerly Advanced X-ray Astrophysics Facility): NASA satellite observatory launched on the space shuttle in July 1999. It is imaging the x-ray sky over the energy range of 0.1 to 10 keV.

charge-coupled device (CCD): an electronic image detector used in modern video cameras and astronomical instruments.

charge-parity (CP) conservation: conservation of properties under a reflection in space and interchange of particle with antiparticle

classical: a general term meaning nonquantum mechanical.

closed universe: a finite-volume universe resulting from the gravitational pull of a high density of matter. It may be visualized as the three-dimensional analogue of the surface of a sphere—if one travels in any direction, one eventually returns to the same place.

cluster of galaxies: a grouping of from tens to thousands of galaxies held together by gravity.

COBE: NASA's COsmic Background Explorer satellite was launched in November 1989; it made precision measurements of the spectrum of the microwave background radiation and discovered tiny variations in its intensity across the sky that arose due to small variations in the density of matter.

compact object: compact objects are the remnants of stars that have burned all of their nuclear fuel, forming white dwarfs, neutron stars, or black holes. The extreme gravitational fields near the stars make them valuable as physical laboratories for studying the gravitational force itself.

compactification: the latest versions of string theory involve an 11-dimensional space. In order for the theory to be consistent with the 4-dimensional space we experience, the extra space dimensions of string theory must curl up into a tiny geometrical space, whose size should be comparable to the string length. This process is known as compactification.

condensate: the macroscopic occupation of a single quantum state, as in a low temperature trapped atomic gas of bosons. When used by particle physicists, it describes the lowest energy state of a system when it is not empty, but rather is filled with a particular nonzero value for some field.

cosmic microwave background (CMB) radiation: the residual light from the big bang. Although the CMB is nearly uniform, there are tiny fluctuations in its temperature due to variations in the density of the early universe. These tiny fluctuations grew to form galaxies.

cosmic rays: protons, nuclei of heavy atoms, and possibly other particles that have been accelerated to high energies by astrophysical processes in the universe and impinge upon Earth.

cosmological constant Λ: the energy density associated with the vacuum (empty space). Recent astronomical observations suggest that there is a net energy associated with the vacuum. If there is a positive vacuum energy, then the expansion of the universe will eventually accelerate and our descendants will find themselves in a nearly empty universe.

cosmology: the study of the contents, structure, and evolution of the universe from the beginning of time to the infinite future.

critical density: the mean density that leads to a spatially uncurved ("flat") universe; higher density universes are positively curved (like the surface of a sphere) and lower density universes are negatively curved (like the surface of a saddle).

cross section: in nuclear or particle physics, the probability that a particular interaction will take place between particles.

curvature: the bending or warping of space and time, predicted by general relativity and theories like it.

DAMA: the DArk MAtter experiment based at the Gran Sasso laboratory in Italy, which has reported unconfirmed evidence for the signature of dark matter particles in the halo.

dark energy: an as-yet-unknown form of energy that pervades the universe and whose gravity is repulsive. Its presence was inferred from the discovery that the expansion of the universe is accelerating, and these observations suggest that about 70 percent of the total density of matter plus energy is in this form. One explanation for dark energy is Einstein's cosmological constant.

dark halo: the roughly spherical distribution of dark matter that surrounds a galaxy.

dark matter: matter that does not emit enough light or other radiation to be observed directly. Most of the matter in the universe is dark. Cold dark matter is made of particles (e.g., axions or neutralinos) that move slowly compared with the speed of light; hot dark matter is made of particles (e.g., neutrinos) that move at nearly the speed of light.

density fluctuations: variations in the density of matter from place to place in the universe. The universe is not uniform.

dragging of inertial frames: a general relativistic phenomenon predicted to occur near rotating masses, in which freely falling laboratories would be dragged slightly around the body. One consequence is that a gyroscope in such a laboratory would precess with respect to the direction it would point in empty space.

Einstein's equation: a mathematical equation written down by Einstein in 1915 to describe how matter and energy curve space and time. This curvature accounts for gravity, superseding Newton's theory of a gravitational force, which remains a good approximation only when gravity is weak.

electromagnetic spectrum: total range of wavelengths or frequencies of electromagnetic radiation. Radiation can be represented as electric and magnetic fields vibrating with a characteristic wavelength or frequency. Long wavelengths (low frequencies) correspond to radio radiation; intermediate wavelengths, to millimeter and infrared radiation; short wavelengths (high frequencies), to visible and ultraviolet light; and extremely short wavelengths, to x rays and gamma rays. Most astronomical observations measure some form of electromagnetic radiation.

epoch: a period characterized by the dominance of a particular physical process, such as the formation of the light elements from protons and neutrons.

epoch of photon decoupling: see epoch of recombination.

epoch of recombination: the time when electrons and nuclei were combining to form atoms and the universe was 1,100 times smaller than its present size; also called the epoch of photon decoupling and the epoch of atom formation.

equation of state: the equation that describes how the pressure and density of a substance are related. Stars remain in equilibrium by balancing the inward pull of gravity against the outward pressure force, so the equation of state must be known to construct theoretical models of stars.

equivalence principle: a fundamental principle of general relativity, one of whose consequences is that all objects (and light) fall in a gravitational field in the same way independent of their internal structure or other properties. This universality of free fall is one of the most accurately verified principles in physics.

eV: an electron-volt, a measure of energy equal to that gained by an electron passing through a potential difference of 1 volt; also a unit of particle mass when divided by the speed of light (c) squared. Electrons have a mass of about 0.511 MeV/c^2 (million electron-volts); protons have a mass of about 938 GeV/c^2 (billion electron-volts).

event horizon: the surface of a black hole. It is a one-way membrane, allowing matter or signals to flow in but not out.

Fermilab: The U.S. Department of Energy's Fermi National Accelerator Laboratory, located in Batavia, Illinois.

fermion: particles with the property that only one can occupy a quantum state (the Pauli exclusion principle). Such particles have half-integer values of spin.

flat universe: a universe where space is uncurved and described by the geometry of Euclid.

forces of nature: the four basic forces of physics: gravity, electromagnetism, and the weak and strong interactions.

freeze-out: the disequilibrium by which relics are formed in the universe.

galaxy: a large assemblage of stars. Our own galaxy, the Milky Way, contains 10^{11} stars.

gamma ray: electromagnetic radiation more energetic than x rays.

gamma-ray bursts: bursts of gamma rays from cosmic sources observed by detectors on satellites. Several hundred are detected per year, and they range in duration from fractions of a second to several seconds. Most gamma ray bursts come from objects at cosmological distances.

general relativity: Einstein's theory of gravity in which the gravity is the curved geometry of space and time.

gluon: a massless particle that carries the strong force.

grand unification era: the era when the universe cooled sufficiently for gravity to be described by Einstein's general relativity theory, but where the temperature was still sufficiently high that the other remaining three forces of nature remained unified.

grand unified theories: theories that combine the strong, electromagnetic, and weak interactions into one unified theory.

gravitational collapse instability: the process whereby a small lump in an expanding universe can grow under gravity, pulling in surrounding matter and ultimately collapsing to form an object like a galaxy or cluster of galaxies.

gravitational lens: an object in which rays of light from a distant astronomical source are deflected by the gravitational pull of an intermediate mass that may be a galaxy or a cluster of galaxies. The deflection causes a distortion in the image of the distant source and sometimes also leads to multiple images.

gravitational lensing: a consequence of Einstein's general relativity theory is that the path of light rays can be bent by the presence of matter. Astronomers have observed that the light from a distant galaxy or quasar can be "lensed" by the matter in an intervening galaxy to form multiple and often distorted images of the background object.

gravitational wave: according to general relativity, a ripple in the geometry of space-time propagating as a wave.

gravitational wave background: gravitational waves arriving from so many sources that the individual signals are indistinguishable.

graviton: an as-yet-undetected massless particle that carries the gravitational force.

Great Attractor: a region or structure of huge mass (equivalent to tens of thousands of galaxies) exerting a gravitational pull on the surrounding galaxies, including the Milky Way, proposed to explain the observed movement of these galaxies toward the Hydra-Centaurus superclusters in the southern sky with velocities significantly different from those predicted by Hubble law expansion.

hadron: a strongly interacting particle such as a proton or neutron.

halo: the matter surrounding a galaxy.

Hawking radiation: when the effects of quantum mechanics are included in the analysis of black holes, it turns out that they are not, strictly speaking, black but rather radiate energy. This phenomenon is called Hawking radiation.

horizon: edge of the portion of the universe visible to us. Light signals from beyond this point have not had time to reach Earth yet.

HST: NASA's Hubble Space Telescope, an optical/infrared telescope launched in 1990.

Hubble's law: the principle that any two distant celestial objects (e.g., galaxies) move away from each other at a speed that is proportional to the distance between them, due to the homogenous expansion of space.

hyperon: a subatomic particle that is a quasi-stable member of the class of particles known as baryons and that is more massive than the nucleons (protons and neutrons).

inflationary universe, inflationary paradigm: an extension of the big bang model characterized by a tremendous burst of expansions. The underlying cause of inflation is not known, though there are many models for it based upon particle physics.

infrared: a region of the electromagnetic spectrum with wavelengths longer than visible light. Hot objects typically are very bright at infrared wavelengths.

interferometer, interferometry: interferometer can be used on a single telescope to break up the light into its constituent colors.

intergalactic medium: the material between galaxies.

inverse square law: an interaction that becomes weaker as the inverse square of the distance between objects.

ionized atom: an atom with an excess or deficit of electrons and thus with a net charge. Under terrestrial conditions, most matter has an equal amount of positive and negative charge, so that its net charge is zero.

IRAS: NASA, British, and Dutch Infrared Astronomy Satellite, which was flown in 1983.

isotope: two or more atoms of the same element that have the same number of protons in their nucleus but different numbers of neutrons are known as isotopes. Hydrogen, deuterium and tritium are isotopes of hydrogen. Most elements in nature consists of a mixture of isotopes.

jet: a set of particles produced from the vacuum state by the movement of quarks and gluons with high momentum found in electron-positron annihilation. The energy associated with the quarks and/or gluons ultimately manifests itself in streams of elementary particles which can be detected.

jet, astrophysical: stream of fast-moving material flowing outward from an object such as a young star or a massive central black hole in a galaxy.

K meson or kaon: second least massive meson, made of one s quark and one u or d antiquark.

Keck telescopes: the two largest ground-based (10-meter) optical telescopes, located on Mauna Kea, Hawaii.

Kerr metric solutions: the *Kerr metric* describes space-time around a spinning mass.

laser interferometer: a device that uses laser light to make accurate comparisons of the lengths of two perpendicular paths.

Lense-Thirring effect: synonymous with dragging of inertial frames (q.v.). The effect is named after Josef Lense and Hans Thirring, Austrian physicists who first calculated the general relativistic predictions for dragging in 1918.

LEP: the Large Electron-positron Project. A particle accelerator at CERN (q.v.).

leptons: a class of elementary particles including electrons, muons, and tauons.

LHC: Large Hadron Collider, a large, high-energy particle accelerator project under construction at CERN. It hopes to expose the Higgs particle and/or supersymmetric partner particles.

LIGO: the Laser Interferometer Gravitational-Wave Observatory is an NSF-sponsored project to build and operate two 4-kilometer laser interferometers (q.v.) to detect gravitational waves.

local supercluster: a large flattened structure centered on the Virgo cluster, of which the Milky Way is a member.

magnetars: neutron stars with the largest known magnetic fields in the universe.

MAP satellite: NASA's Microwave Anisotropy Probe, launched in June 2001, designed to accurately map the microwave sky with an angular resolution of 0.2 degrees. At MAP's frequencies (22 to 96 GHz), most of the fluctuations in the microwave sky are due to variations in the cosmic microwave background (q.v.).

matter-antimatter symmetry: when enough energy is concentrated to produce particles in an experiment, equal numbers of matter and antimatter (q.v.) particles are produced. When the antiparticles meet their matter counterparts, they disappear, returning to pure energy. Nothing is added. Nothing is lost. However, some subtle experiments have revealed that this symmetry is not perfect and that there exists a slight bias in matter's favor. This bias translates to just a single proton surviving out of every billion that could have emerged from the big bang. It is from this one in a billion that the universe is made.

MAXIMA: the Millimeter Anisotropy eXperiment Imaging Array (MAXIMA) is a balloon-borne millimeter-wave telescope designed to measure the angular power spectrum of fluctuations in the cosmic microwave background (q.v.) over a wide range of angular scales. Such measurements provide a powerful probe of the early universe.

microlensing: if a small, dark body is directly in the line of sight to a bright background star, the brightness of the background star may appear to increase because of bending of the light rays by the dark body.

neutralino: neutral particles with a spin of one-half, predicted by supersymmetry as counterparts to the photon, the W boson, and the neutral Higgs boson.

neutrino: very light (possibly massless) particle emitted in the process of radioactive decay. There are three species, associated with electrons, muons, and tau-leptons. They interact with ordinary matter through the weak force.

neutrino oscillation: a process whereby neutrinos of one type may be able to change into those of another type and back again if one or more of the types have mass.

neutron star: a star at such a high density and pressure that its atoms have been completely crushed until the nuclei merge and most of the electrons have been squeezed onto the protons, forming neutron-rich material.

Newton's law: Newton's law of gravity, which states that falling and orbiting of a mass in the vicinity of another mass are caused by an attractive force along a line joining them. This theory is the limit of general relativity when speeds are much less than the speed of light and gravitational fields are weak.

nuclear density: the density at which neutrons and protons are packed together inside the nucleus of an atom.

nucleon: neutron or proton.

nucleosynthesis: the process by which the elements are built up from protons and neutrons.

open universe: a negatively curved universe with mean density less than the critical density.

Pauli exclusion principle: The quantum-mechanical principle, applying to fermions but not to bosons, that no two identical particles in a system, such as electrons in an atom or quarks in a hadron, can possess an identical set of quantum numbers. The origin of the Pauli exclusion principle lies in the spin-statistics theorem of relativistic quantum field theory.

phase transition: a change in a feature that characterizes a system. Examples of phase transitions are changes from solid to liquid, liquid to gas, and the reverse changes. Phase transitions can occur by altering such variables as temperature and pressure.

photon: quantum of electromagnetic energy; a unique massless particle that carries the electromagnetic force.

Planck satellite: European Space Agency's Planck satellite, scheduled for launch in 2007. It will measure the microwave sky over a wide range of wavelengths (22 to 900 GHz) with an angular resolution of 0.1 degrees.

Planck scale: a scale related to the unique length that can be constructed from Newton's gravitational constant, the velocity of light, and the quantum of action and that characterizes quantum-mechanical phenomena. Its value is 10^{-33} centimeters. There is a corresponding Planck energy (10^{19} GeV) and Planck time (10^{-43} seconds).

plasma: consists of a gas heated to sufficiently high temperatures that the atoms ionize. The properties of the gas are controlled by electromagnetic forces among constituent ions and electrons, which results in a different type of behavior. Plasma is often considered the fourth state of matter (besides solid, liquid, and gas). Most of the matter in the universe is in the plasma state.

polarization: the strength of the electric field associated with polarized light is stronger along one of the two directions perpendicular to the direction that the light is traveling. Scattered light is always polarized to some degree. The CMB is slightly polarized.

positron: antiparticle of the electron.

precess(ion): a form of motion that occurs when a torque is applied to a rotating body in such a way that it tends to change the direction of axis of rotation. A spinning top rotates, or precesses, around the direction perpendicular to the surface on which it spins.

pulsar: a spinning neutron star that emits radiation in a beam. The sweeping action of the beam causes the object to pulse regularly when viewed by an observer, just as with a lighthouse.

QCD: quantum chromodynamics, the theory that describes the strong force among quarks in a manner analogous to the description of the electromagnetic force by quantum electrodynamics.

QED: quantum electrodynamics, the theory that describes the electromagnetic interaction in the framework of quantum mechanics (q.v.). The particle carrying the electromagnetic force is the photon.

quantum cosmology: the area of physics and astrophysics concerned with a theory of the quantum initial state of the universe and its consequences for observations today.

quantum mechanics: mathematical framework for describing the physics at atomic and smaller length scales, where energy exists in discrete quantum units.

quark-gluon plasma: although today all quarks are bound together in nucleons (protons or neutrons), during the first 10 microseconds after the big bang the temperature of the universe was so high that unbound quarks moved freely in a state of matter called a quark-gluon plasma. It is also possible to artificially create a quark-gluon plasma by colliding two heavy nuclei at very high energies so that the nucleons dissolve into their quarks and gluons parts, such as is being done at RHIC.

quarks: the elementary constituents of mesons and baryons (e.g., neutrons and protons).

quasar: a very compact and extraordinarily luminous source of radiation in the nucleus of a distant galaxy. Quasars are believed to be powered by accretion (q.v.) of gas onto massive black holes.

quasiperiodic oscillations: rapid not-quite-regular variations in the brightness of the x rays emitted by the accretion (q.v.) of matter onto a neutron star or black hole. The nearly periodic variations (that is, the variations are periodic but not perfectly so) are believed to reflect the dynamics of the disk of accreting matter.

radio waves: electromagnetic waves with wavelengths that are very long compared with those of visible light. The radio band is usually considered to include all electromagnetic waves with wavelengths greater than about 1 millimeter.

redshift, z: the shifting of light toward the red end of the spectrum that occurs due to the expansion of the universe. The wavelength of the light received is a factor $(1 + z)$ larger, corresponding to the fact that the universe has grown in size by a factor $(1 + z)$ since the light was emitted.

relativistic: systems with particles moving with velocities close to the velocity of light.

relativity: theoretical framework proposed by Einstein in the early part of the 20th century. There are two relativity theories: special and general.

rest mass energy: the rest mass energy of a body is expressed by the relationship $E = m_0 c^2$, where m_0 is the rest mass of the body and c is the speed of light.

Schwarzschild radius: the location of the "surface" of a black hole, from whose interior it is impossible to escape.

shock waves: a very narrow region of high pressure and temperature formed in a fluid when the fluid flows supersonically over a stationary object or when a projectile flying supersonically passes through a stationary fluid. A shock wave may also be generated by violent disturbances in a fluid, such as occurs near a lightning stroke or a bomb blast.

singularity: a region of infinite gravitational field and infinite space-time curvature. General relativity predicts that this is the ultimate result of gravitational collapse.

SIRTF: NASA's Space Infrared Telescope Facility, an orbiting infrared telescope, is scheduled for launch in 2003.

SLAC: Stanford Linear Accelerator Center in Stanford, California; the electron and positron linear accelerator there has an energy of 50 GeV.

SNO: the Sudbury Neutrino Observatory, located 6,800 feet underground in a mine in Ontario, Canada, is a heavy-water Cherenkov detector designed to detect neutrinos produced by fusion reactions in the Sun.

solar flare: a bright eruption of hot gas in the Sun's photosphere.

solar mass: the mass of the Sun.

solar neutrino: fusion reactions in the core of the Sun produce a huge flux of neutrinos called solar neutrinos.

space-time: the four dimensional continuum in which we live, consisting of the three dimensions of space and one dimension of time. General relativity (q.v.) is concerned with the curvature (q.v.) of space-time.

spatial interferometer: combines beams of light from different telescopes to synthesize the aperture of a single large telescope. Spatial interferometry is the main technique used by astronomers to map sources at high resolution and to measure their positions with high precision.

special relativity: Einstein's theory of space-time structure, in which Newton's notion of absolute time is abandoned to account for the experimental fact that the speed of light is a universal constant and does not depend on the relative motion between the observer and the light source.

spectroscopy: a technique whereby the light from astronomical objects is broken up into its constituent colors. Radiation from the different chemical elements that make up an object can be distinguished, giving information about the abundance of these elements and their physical state.

SQUID: a Superconducting Quantum Interference Device is a very sensitive device for magnetic field detection developed for both traditional low-temperature superconductors and the new high-temperature superconductors.

standard candle: a celestial object whose intrinsic brightness is known or can be estimated by some physical principle and whose observed brightness is therefore useful as a tool to measure distance.

Standard Model: the theory that summarizes the current picture of the field of elementary-particle physics. It includes three generations of quarks and leptons, the electroweak theory of weak and electromagnetic forces, and the quantum chromodynamic theory of the strong force. It does not include answers to some basic questions such as how to unify electroweak forces with the strong or gravitational forces.

string theory: a new physical theory that appears to be both a consistent quantum theory of gravity and a unified theory of all particles and forces.

strong (color) force: one of the four fundamental forces, along with gravity, the electromagnetic force, and the weak nuclear force, that acts between elementary particles of matter.

strong interaction (or strong nuclear force): the force felt by baryons and mesons that holds nucleons together in atomic nuclei. Once thought to be fundamental, the strong nuclear force is now described as a residual effect of the color force that binds quarks into mesons and baryons.

superconductivity: the absence of measurable electrical resistance in certain substances. First discovered in 1911 in mercury, superconductivity is now known to occur in some 26 metallic elements and many compounds and alloys. The temperature below which a substance becomes superconducting is called the transition temperature (or critical temperature).

superfluidity: the property of a low temperature system from liquid helium to atomic Bose-Einstein condensates to nuclear matter in neutron stars that enables fluid flow without friction.

supermassive black hole: very large black holes (q.v.) with masses one million to one billion times the mass of our Sun that appear to be found at the core of most galaxies. Supermassive black holes are thought to be the engines that power quasars. Our own galaxy has a 2 million-solar-mass black hole at its center.

supersymmetry: a space-time symmetry that would imply the existence of partners to all elementary particles, with quantum spins of one-half a unit higher or lower. Often used in constructing theories that unify gravity with the three other forces.

synchrotron radiation: electromagnetic radiation that is emitted by charged particles moving at relativistic speeds in circular orbits in a magnetic field. Much of the microwave radiation from celestial radio sources outside the galaxy is believed to originate from electrons moving in curved paths in celestial magnetic fields; it is also called synchrotron radiation.

thermal spectrum: the characteristic distribution of radiation as a function of frequency that is emitted by a body at a well-defined temperature, also called a black-body or Planckian spectrum.

time reversal invariance: or T symmetry, holds that the laws of physics should be the same when time is run backwards.

topological defects: Symmetry-breaking phase transitions occur in many physical systems. In some of these systems, as the phase transition occurs, regions of space can become trapped in the wrong or unbroken phase. Examples include the vortices produced during the superfluid or superconducting phase transitions and also cosmic strings in the early universe. Such regions are called *topological defects* and give us an experimental handle on the nonequilibrium dynamics of the transition.

Tully-Fisher relation: a method to determine galactic distances. Big, luminous galaxies rotate faster than small, faint ones. The connection between the two is given by the Tully-Fisher relation.

Type Ia supernova: thermonuclear explosion of a white dwarf star caused by the accretion of material from a binary companion. Type IA supernovae (SneIa) can be used as standard candles to chart the universe.

Type II supernova: a gigantic explosion that signals the death of a massive star. Often, the explosion leaves behind a neutron star; in other cases it may produce a black hole.

uncertainty principle: the principle that it is not possible to know with unlimited precision both the position of a particle and its momentum.

unification: the concept that two or more forces that seem distinct in today's universe could, at higher energies (or temperatures), merge to become one force.

universality of free fall: a central prediction of general relativity that the gravitational acceleration of a small object depends only on its location in space, not on any properties of the object itself.

universe: all of space and time taken together.

vacuum: a space in which there is a low pressure of gas, i.e., relatively few atoms or molecules. A perfect vacuum would contain no atoms or molecules but is unobtainable, as all the materials that surround such a space have a finite vapor pressure and give off atoms into the void.

vacuum energy (sometimes called "Einstein's cosmological constant"): quantum physics requires "empty space" to be filled with particles and antiparticles being continually created and annihilated. If the energy density associated with vacuum energy is not zero, it could be the dark energy that is causing the expansion of the universe to accelerate.

virtual process or particle: one that is physically forbidden in classical mechanics but allowed by quantum mechanics.

VLA: the Very Large Array, an array in New Mexico of 27 radio telescopes capable of adjustable spacing along a Y-shaped track, up to a radius of 27 kilometers.

VLBA: Very Long Baseline Array, a newly completed radio interferometer operated by the National Radio Astronomy Observatory and capable of producing images with angular resolution of one-thousandth of an arcsecond (q.v.).

W boson: particle that carries the charged weak force.

weak interactions (force): the interactions of elementary particles that are responsible for radioactive decay.

white dwarf star: a very small star that is the remnant core of a star that has completed fusion in its core. The Sun will become a white dwarf. White dwarfs are typically composed primarily of carbon, have about the radius of Earth, and do not significantly evolve further.

x-ray binary: a double star in which one of the stars accretes matter from its binary companion (q.v.) and emits a copious quantity of x rays. The x-ray-emitting star is either a black hole (q.v.) or a neutron star (q.v.).

XMM-Newton: a European x-ray space mission.

Z boson: particle that carries the neutral weak force (q.v.).